Vandas

Vandas

Their Botany, History, and Culture

by Martin R. Motes, Ph.D.

with photography by
Alan L. Hoffman, D.D.S.

Timber Press
Portland, Oregon

Copyright © 1997 by Timber Press, Inc.
All rights reserved.

Reprinted 2000

Printed in Hong Kong

TIMBER PRESS, INC.
The Haseltine Building
133 S.W. Second Avenue, Suite 450
Portland, Oregon 97204, U.S.A.

Library of Congress Cataloging-in-Publication Data

Motes, Martin R.
  Vandas / their botany, history, and culture / by Martin R. Motes ;
    p. cm.
  Includes bibliographical references (p.   ) and index.
  ISBN 0-88192-376-1
  1. Vanda. I. Orchid culture. I. Title.
SB409.8.V36M67   1997
635.9'3415–dc20   96-32199
                                                            CIP

What they undertook to do
They brought to pass;
All things hang like a drop of dew
Upon a blade of grass.

—Yeats,
Gratitude to the Unknown Instructors

Contents

Color plates follow page 48

Preface

My love of orchids began, not with vandas, but with cattleyas. This was true for most growers in the 1950s. Vandas were then considered *botanical* orchids: plants grown as novelties for their unusual forms and for the color of their flowers. These exotics had been imported to Florida from Hawaii and Singapore, and rapidly found niches in gardens, patios, and shade houses. If the form and carriage of the early vandas often seemed somewhat alien to the sensibilities of cattleya growers, their fragrance and their novel color range were certainly appealing. Even more appealing for many of us were their vigor, ease of cultivation, and freedom from pests. They were also the most affordable of new orchids, since they matured in 3 – 4 years from seed. One could buy a very small, inexpensive seedling that would bloom after just 2 years—long before a cattleya of the same age.

Vandas have been steadily improved over the past 30 years, with much of the early work having been done in Hawaii and Florida, and many of the later developments having been made in Thailand. With the improved quality of vandas has come a wider acceptance of the inherent aesthetics of the genus—and for good reason: modern vandas are the most spectacular of all cultivated orchids.

Properly grown, no other orchid produces such a profusion of large, vivid flowers. The kaleidoscopic range of colors in modern *Vanda* hybrids is unmatched by any other orchid genus. Furthermore, the free-flowering nature of the plants (some bloom as often as 6 or more times per year) and the durability of the flowers (they often last 4–8 weeks on the plant) exceed that of any other large-flowered type of orchid. This of course means, in effect, that vandas are in bloom for much of the year, and for longer than any other major orchid genus. Their ease of cultivation and the simplicity of care in baskets (which reduces repotting to a minimum) also places vandas leagues ahead of other orchid genera.

All of these factors have contributed to vandas' becoming one of the most popular genera among growers in tropical and subtropical areas and, increasingly (as their care is mastered), in temperate greenhouses. The availability of top-quality *Vanda* hybrids from Thailand, as well as from Florida and Hawaii, has stimulated a resurgence of interest in the cultivation and connoisseurship of these plants, which are no longer considered *botanical* or of minor horticultural interest. Vandas were the last of our major genera to be developed to any significant degree.

This book seeks to provide a comprehensive horticultural treatment of the genus, including a much-needed, in-depth treatment of the botany, history, breeding, and culture of vandas, which goes well beyond the cursory treatment found in general literature on the genus. The focus and tone is not purely scientific, but addressed rather to the interests and needs of the advanced horticulturist.

The history of vandas' introduction to cultivation and of their subsequent cultural development is presented together with an overview of the taxonomy and botany of the genus. But the emphasis has been placed on aspects of the subject that are likely to be of interest or use to those working with the living plants in their greenhouses and gardens.

Observations on the relationships between various species are based upon 35 years of practical observation of the plants in cultivation. That experience also informs the sections on cultivation, care, and disease and pest control. I am indebted to the many greenhouse growers of vandas in various parts of the United States who have allowed me to observe their growing methods and shared with me their observations and experience on the cultivation of these plants under temperate-zone conditions. It is my hope that the present synopsis of that shared experience will offer something in return—not only to all of them, but also to their fellows, pioneering the successful cultivation of vandas in northern climates.

This book will have succeeded if it brings together a body of knowledge on the history, botany, and cultivation of vandas that can serve as a primer for all those who seek to become adept in the knowledge of the plants. The hybridization of vandas has achieved a high degree of sophistication, and yet there is arguably no other group of orchids with so much untapped potential. As knowledge of the plants' marvelous qualities spreads, along with knowledge of their successful cultivation, we can expect dramatic advances in the development of improved forms, new color types, and even hardier, more vigorous plants. I hope the following discussion will help us toward those goals.

Martin R. Motes, Ph.D.
Motes Orchids

Acknowledgments

Without the help and support of my wife, Mary, this book would never have been written. Her assistance with editing and typing, and her advice on style, were indispensable. My friend Ann Reaben Prospero, who typed and edited the first draft, was instrumental in moving the book toward its final form. The contribution made by Dr. Eric Christenson was immeasurable. He offered constant and generous advice on all aspects of the botany of vandas, and in rendering the science of these plants intelligible to me, he has also, I sincerely hope, made it intelligible to my readers. Dr. Kiat Tan generously allowed me access to the herbarium at the Singapore Botanical Gardens. Dr. Phillip Cribb was likewise generous in allowing me to use the facilities at Kew. The staff at the herbarium at Bogor, Indonesia, and the herbarium staff at the British Museum also assisted me in ensuring botanical accuracy. Jay Mullen, Randy Robinson, Jack Webster, and countless other temperate zone growers helped me to understand that these plants are most successfully grown under temperate conditions. My editor, Sally Roth, deserves special thanks for guiding book and author through the storms (both literal and figurative) of Hurricane Andrew and the fungicide Benlate DF. Readers should also be aware of the magnificent contribution made by Alan Hoffman. Undaunted by the merciless attentions of the mosquitoes of our South Florida greenhouses, he has produced what I believe to be the finest pictorial record of the genus *Vanda* ever made.

One

The Discovery
of Vandas
and Their Introduction
to the West

Seventeenth-century travelers to the Far East were the first foreign observers to describe vandas for the western world. In 1613, Alvim Semedo, a Jesuit who traveled in China, wrote of *tiao hua*, hanging flowers or air plants, which could exist for months suspended in air. These may have been vandas and aerides. The first specific *Vanda* to be recorded in Western literature, known in the vernacular as *Ponnampou-maravara*, was listed in *Hortus Indicus Malabaricus* (1703) by H. A. Rheede tot Draakenstein, a late-17th-century governor of Malabar. Today that plant is known as *Vanda spathulata* K. Spreng (Plate 1-1), or, more correctly, as *Taprobanea spathulata* E. A. Christ.

A German botanist working for the Dutch East India Company, Georg Everhard Rumphius (1637–1706), recorded six species known today as *Vanda helvola* Blume, *V. insignis* Blume (Plate 1-2), *V. concolor* Blume, *V. furva* Lindley (now considered a synonym of *V. concolor*), *V. limbata* Blume (Plate 1-3), and *V. tricolor* Lindley (Karl Ludwig Blume's *V. suaveolens*) (Plate 1-4). His work *Herbarium amboinensis* (1741–50) appeared long after his death and was, of course, in non-

Linnaean form. Linnaeus himself described a species of *Vanda* as *Epidendrum spathulatum* in the first edition of *Species Plantarum* (1753) and another as *Epidendrum furvum* in the second edition (1762).

The Genus *Vanda*

Even though westerners continued to encounter vandas in Southeast Asia, the genus was not established until 1795, by Sir William Jones in *Asiatic Researches*, based on *Vanda roxburghii* Robert Brown (i.e., *V. tessellata* [Roxburgh] W. J. Hook. ex G. Don.) (Plate 1-5). Robert Brown formally described this plant in 1820, referring it to Jones's concept; hence, in modern terms the genus is *Vanda* Jones ex R. Br. The generic epithet *Vanda* is from the Sanskrit word for the type species. The specific epithet honors Dr. William Roxburgh, the director of the Calcutta Botanical Gardens from 1797 to 1814.

Roxburgh sent plants of this species and others to both Conrad Loddiges and Sir Joseph Banks. Banks flowered it for the first time in England in the autumn of 1817 "in his stove at Spring-grove" (Cribb 1981). "Stoves" were darkly painted greenhouses that were heated by furnaces to stifling temperatures in a misguided attempt to reproduce tropical conditions. Vandas were among the best adapted of tropical orchids to the abominably hot and humid conditions of these stove houses, which were the first attempt at orchid culture in England. Their tendency to produce abundant aerial roots outside the primitive composts of the time saved them from untimely deaths due to fungal disease.

Vanda spathulata, another classic stove-house plant, was assigned to the genus *Vanda* in 1826. In the late 1830s, John Lindley began his work on the genus, describing *V. alpina* and *V. lamellata* in 1838, *V. cristata* in 1842, *V. hindsii* in 1843, *V. parviflora* (i.e., *V. testacea* [Lindl.] Reichb.f.) in 1844, and *V. coerulea* Griff. ex Lindl. and *V. tricolor* in 1847. In 1848, Karl Ludwig Blume published *Rumphia*, an updating of Rumphius's respected work into Linnaean form, which added *V. furva*, *V. helvola*, *V. insignis*, *V. concolor*, and *V. limbata* to the known species. The genus had grown to a size and acceptance that warranted serious delineation.

Lindley's Concept of the Genus

Lindley published the first monograph of the genus in 1853 as one of his *Folia Orchidacea*. He defines the genus as follows:

> The limits of this genus are very difficult to ascertain; they are here defined by a saccate or calcarate lip continuous with the column, a truncate rostellum, and two or four pollen-masses attached to a broad caudicle having a large circular gland. It is very near *Luisia*, which is better known by its habit than by any very satisfactory peculiarity of structure, except having a very short broad caudicle, and thin gland. Probably V. *Lowei* at least will be hereafter separated, if other species agreeing with it in its long drooping racemes and simple unguiculate lip should be discovered. The genus, as it now stands, may be divided into the following sections:
>
> 1. *Fieldia* Lip obscurely auriculate, incurved, entire, concave at the base, with a strong tooth at or above its middle. Pollen-masses four.
>
> 2. *Euvanda* Lip auriculate, straight, variously lobed, spurred, even or furrowed (usually with a tooth or callus in front of the spur).
>
> 3. *Lamellaria* Lip auriculate, straight, variously lobed or entire, spurred, bearing from one to three perpendicular plates.
>
> 4. *Anota* Lip without auricles, contracted and lobed at the point, spurred, with a pair of hairy elevated veins.
>
> 5. *Cristatae* Lip auriculate, straight or recurved, quite naked, saccate or excavated at the base.

Of these five sections, two are referred to other genera by 20th-century botanists: *Fieldia* to *Vandopsis* (Plates 1-6 and 1-7) and the related genus *Dimorphorchis*, and *Anota* to *Rhynchostylis* (Plate 1-8). With the four species of these two sections eliminated, from a modern view 21 remained in the genus as defined by Lindley in 1853. Of these, three are now referred to other genera: *Vanda cathcartii* is now reckoned *Esmeralda cathcartii*; *V. sulingii*, *Armodorum sulingii*; and *V. teres*, *Papilionanthe teres* (Plate 1-9). Two others are synonyms of listed species: *V. fuscoviridis* is *V. furva*, and Lindley's *V. suavis* is considered *V. tricolor*. At least one additional species, *V. bicolor*, is dubious. By the mid-19th century, only 14 to 15 valid species of *Vanda* were known.

Lindley's concept of the genus was well formed and well founded, but still evolving. He relegated, to four other genera, seven other species previously attributed to the genus (including five species he had previously included in *Vanda*).

With Lindley's synopsis of the genus, *Vanda* became a clearly established concept from the mid-19th century onward. His sections *Euvanda*, *Lamellaria*, and *Cristatae* form the modern basis of the genus, with only the last section subject to redefinition by Leslie Garay as *Trudelia*, a concept not yet firmly established. The attribution to *Vanda* of species that properly belong in other genera continued well into the 20th century, but Lindley's basic concept of the genus has prevailed. All of the species generally accepted as *Vanda* by contemporary botanists fit Lindley's definition and could be placed in one of his sections.

Additions to the Genus

In the 1850s and '60s, four more valid species were added to the genus: *Vanda stangeana* Reichb.f. in 1858, *V. lilacina* Teijsm. & Binn. in 1862, *V. bensonii* Batem. in 1866, and *V. denisoniana* Benson & Reichb.f. in 1869. From the 19th-century perspective, *Vanda denisoniana* was the most significant of them. The pale yellow *Vanda denisoniana* caused quite a stir as the novelty of a "white" *Vanda* aroused the orchid community. It was thought to be a "very chaste and desirable species" (Williams 1894) in Victorian England, and one clone received a First Class Certificate (FCC) in 1869 from the Royal Horticultural Society.

Most of the valid species published in the mid- to late 19th century were described by Heinrich Gustav Reichenbach, the son of the famous German taxonomist, Heinrich Gott Reichenbach. After his friend Lindley's death, Reichenbach became the undisputed authority on orchid taxonomy. In addition to *Vanda stangeana* and *V. denisoniana*, Reichenbach described *V. hastifera* in 1877, *Euanthe sanderiana* in 1882, and *V. dearei* in 1886, most of these being published and illustrated in the *Gardeners' Chronicle* (for which he wrote a weekly article from 1865 till 1889). The Royal Horticultural Society (RHS) continues to register hybrids as derived from *Vanda sanderiana*. Most botanists, however, place the species in its own genus, and this modern practice is followed in this book. There are many botanical differences between *Euanthe* and *Vanda*, and these are discussed in Chapter 2. Their equally important horticultural and aesthetic differences are described in Chapters 4 and 8.

In the 1890s, Joseph Dalton Hooker added two species to the genus, *Vanda pumila* (Plate 1-10) (1890) and *V. thwaitesii* (1898). In his *Flora of British India*, he divided the genus into three of Lindley's sections, *Euvanda*, *Anota*, and *Cristatae*, eliminating Lindley's section *Fieldia* and combining *Lamellaria* with *Euvanda*.

Robert Allen Rolfe's additions to the genus began in the 1890s with the publication of *Vanda roeblingiana* and *V. celebica*, and continued into the first two decades of the 20th century with the publication of *V. gibbsiae* in 1914 and *V. luzonica* Loher ex Rolfe in 1915. Johannes Jacobus Smith was also active in this period and on into the 1920s and '30s, publishing *V. foetida* (1906), *V. arcuata* (1907), *V. lombokensis* (1925), *V. saxatilis* (1926), and *V. devoogtii* (1932).

In addition to Rolfe and Smith, other botanists described the bulk of the remaining valid species of *Vanda* during the early part of the century. Friedrich Richard Schlechter described *V. leucostele* and *V. sumatrana* in 1911; Achille Eugene Finet, *V. liouvillei* in 1912; Henry Nicholas Ridley, *V. punctata* in 1923; and Oakes Ames and Eduardo Quisumbing, *V. merrillii* in 1930.

With the exception of Richard Eric Holttum's *Vanda scandens*, which may prove to be merely a variety of *V. hastifera*, no new species were added to the genus for over three decades until *V. subconcolor* was published by T. Tang and F. T. Wang in 1974. Ten years later came the publication of two new species, *V. javieriae*, D. Tiu, and *V. jainii*, A. S. Chauhan. While *V. javieriae* appears to be a distinct addition to the genus, *V. jainii* may prove to be merely a variety of either *V. cristata* or *V. alpina*, or perhaps a hybrid form involving these closely related species. One more species has been added to the genus by Eric Christenson, who transferred *Aerides flabellata* to the genus as *V. flabellata* (Rolfe ex Downie) E. A. Christenson (Plate 1-11). The rather singular *V. spathulata* has been assigned by Christenson to a new genus, *Taprobanea*.

More *Vanda* species may well be discovered, particularly since parts of the Philippines and the Indonesian archipelago, as well as Indochina, are still not fully explored. The seldom seen Indonesian species may in time prove to be a more diverse group than is presently thought.

Conservation of Species Vandas

One danger that looms over *Vanda* species is the rapid destruction of their habitats due to logging and the expansion of agriculture in the Old World tropics. The current lack of horticultural interest in the species themselves and in their primary hybrids exacerbates this danger. The decline in horticultural popularity is easily apparent. Species and varieties of vandas that would have caused sensations in Victorian England have been introduced without creating the least interest in horticultural circles. Moreover, horticulturally significant species such as *Vanda insignis* have virtually disappeared from cultivation.

This shortsightedness could easily lead to the elimination of many species that have never been widely grown in any case. Some species are also being driven out of cultivation by hybrids assumed, by those unfamiliar with the species, to be *superior* forms.

This appears clearly to be happening with *Vanda coerulea*, *V. luzonica*, *V. merrillii*, and *V. tessellata*. Indeed, as a group, *Vanda* species are perhaps more seriously endangered than any other large-flowered genus of orchids. One can only hope that their intrinsic beauty will again come to be appreciated before it disappears forever. The task of ensuring that these handsome species plants are preserved in cultivation is one for both horticulturists and botanical gardens.

Two

The Botany
of Vandas

Vandas belong to a large, very recently evolved group of plants that are commonly referred to as vandaceous orchids. Gunnar Seidenfaden (1988) proposed the term *Aeridinae* for this group, but the more usual botanical term is *Sarcanthinae*. Following the system proposed by Robert L. Dressler (1981), this would be expressed as the sub-tribe Sarcanthinae of the tribe Vandeae.

The plant morphology of this exceptionally large group is remarkably homogenous, falling into a few distinctive variants of the monopodial, fanlike growth from a single central point. In the older botanical view, which still persists in horticultural literature, all of these variations of growth habit, from terete- to broad-leaved, are frequently met in a single genus. In modern taxonomy, flower structure is the major criterion for grouping species and genera. This complex diversity, and the sheer number of genera (100 or more) and species (1300) involved, has deterred many modern botanists from attempting a comprehensive organization of Sarcanthinae. Michael Wirth, a student of Dressler's, has referred to the sub-tribe as a taxonomic "black hole." Much botanical attention has been focused on the Sarcanthinae. Both the genus *Vanda* and the sub-tribe to which it belongs will doubtless continue to provide a fertile field, as it were, for taxonomists to plow.

The group continues to present many taxonomic difficulties for botanists. The simplicity of the obviously very successful monopodial growth habit, with its clear variation from broad to terete leaves, initially led botanists to lump large groups of species together on the basis of rather gross floral similarities. This approach is exemplified by R. E. Holttum's (1964) statement that vegetative types, from strap-leaved to terete, could be found in several genera. This was also traditionally the case with *Vanda*. In the older view, following George Bentham's emphasis on vegetative characteristics, the genus could be divided into three parts: (1) strap-leaf (all those with broadly open, leathery, or fleshy leaves or deeply V-shaped leaves; i.e., vandas and *Euanthe sanderiana*); (2) semiterete (those with rounded but deeply furrowed leaves; i.e., the modern genus *Holcoglossum*); and (3) terete (those with pencil-shaped leaves; i.e., the modern genus *Papilionanthe*). Now that botanists have examined the genera closely allied to *Vanda*, this older view is less commonly held. The importance of pollinators and their relationship to lip structure in determining species is now well established. Over 150 species that are now distributed among 20 genera (with a 21st and 22nd proposed) at one time or another have been assigned to *Vanda*. As knowledge of the group develops and further examination proceeds, it is almost certain that further genera will be segregated from *Vanda*.

The Six Groupings of *Vanda*

For the purpose of this book and for horticultural use, *Vanda* is best thought of as comprising the following six groups:

1. *Euanthe*	Composed of one species, *Euanthe sanderiana*.
2. *Cristata* or *Trudelia*	Composed of *Vanda cristata*, *V. alpina*, *V. pumila*, *V. griffithii*, and *Trudelia chlorosantha*.

3. *Coerulea*   Composed of one species,
                         Vanda coerulea.

4. *Testacea*   Composed of *Vanda testacea*,
                         V. coerulescens, and *V. lilacina*.

5. *Spathulata* or   Composed of
   Taprobanea   *Vanda spathulata.*

6. *Tessellata*   Composed of the 30 species most
                         closely related to the type species.

This division recognizes the exclusion of the terete species now included in the genus *Papilionanthe* and the semiterete species (such as *Vanda amesiana*) now included in the genus *Holcoglossum*. Three of these six divisions, *Euanthe*, *Trudelia*, and *Taprobanea*, have been assigned to other genera by some authors. Two others, *V. coerulea* and the species allied to *V. testacea*, almost certainly may be given separate generic rank. The genus as now circumscribed needs much critical re-examination.

The characteristics that unite these disparate groups are best summed up in Seidenfaden (1988):

The floral structure is among the more simple within the sub-tribe, and the genus is often considered as primitive. Usually, the plants have very thick roots, the stem is quite stout with short internodes, the leaves, at an acute angle to the stem, are strap-shaped and with some exceptions characterized by the praemorse leaf tips; you can usually "feel" a *Vanda* by this feature, which is rare elsewhere. The inflorescences are simple and more or less erect, with rather few well-spaced, often long-pedicelled, medium to large, usually quite fleshy flowers. Sepals and petals nearly equal or the sepals broader, narrowed to the base, the edges more or less reflexed, often twisted or wavy, tessellation is common in the genus. The lip is unmovably attached to a very short, indistinct column

foot, short-spurred and three-lobed. There are no ornaments inside the spur, but the mid-lobe often has low
rounded longitudinal swellings or keels, and most often
there are one or two small calli at its base at entrance to
the spur. The column is short and stout, laterally broad-
ening towards base, the rostellum prolongation short,
broad and simple, bidentate after the removal of the
viscidium, which is large transversely elliptic, the stipes
short and broad, narrowing below the pollinia, not much
longer than the diameter of the pollinia, of which there
are two, cleft.

All of the species in the six groups (*Vanda spathulata* being something of an exception) conform broadly to this definition. Beyond that
broad definition, however, subtle differences emerge. If one takes the
type species, *V. tessellata*, and the species most closely allied to it as a
norm (all of which possess broad strap leaves, three-lobed, distinctly
spurred lips as long or nearly as long as their petals, and elongating stems
which freely produce adventitious roots), the distinctiveness of the other
groups comes into clearer perspective.

The *Euanthe* Division

Consider first one of the divisions that has already been assigned to
its own genera in *Euanthe*. Although initially *E. sanderiana* has the
"feel" of a *Vanda*, i.e., roughly strap-shaped leaves with praemorse leaf
tips, the actual leaf shape, leaf carriage, rooting pattern, petal shape, and
lip morphology all argue for a separate genus. (The case for *E. sanderiana* is made in detail in Chapter 4.) Only the vast nomenclature confusion of creating new generic epithets for all of its hybrids militate against
Euanthe's becoming a universally accepted concept. Perhaps this could
be alleviated by conserving the abbreviated *V.* for the vast array of
vandanthes (hybrids between *Euanthe* and *Vanda*) and creating a new
abbreviation, *Vd.*, for true vandas and their hybrids. The same principle
could be applied to the hybrid genera, i.e., *Ascovandanthe*.

The *Cristata* or *Trudelia* Division

The species related to *Vanda cristata* (Plate 2-1) were first identified as a separate entity by J. Lindley, who gave them the sectional title *Cristatae*. A new genus, *Trudelia*, has been proposed around this group. *Trudelia*, as defined by Leslie Garay and expanded by K. Senghas, is composed of five species. Of these, four were originally described as vandas: *V. alpina, V. cristata, V. griffithii, and V. pumila*. The fifth is a new concept, *Trudelia chlorosantha*, with a sixth, *V. jainii*, to be added if the specific concept and the genus persist. One major problem with the taxonomy of this group is that the lip morphology and coloration vary greatly, not only between individual plants from the same populations, but also from flower to flower on the same inflorescence, and, markedly, from year to year on different flowerings of the same individual. Though herbarium specimens remain forever immutable, the living specimens of this group can be observed to display great diversity. The differences between *V. pumila* and *V. cristata* are clear-cut and indisputable. *Vanda alpina* very closely resembles *V. cristata*—some varieties of which Lindley notes are very similar—but lacks distinct horns at the lip apex and is considerably smaller. *Vanda chlorosantha* is also a distinct concolor, greenish yellow flower.

The large, fleshy lips of *Vanda* section *Cristatae* seem to parallel the intricate lips of the Indonesian species *V. hastifera* and *V. crassiloba* as well as such large-lipped species as *V. stangeana, V. insignis*, and to a lesser degree *V. denisoniana*, all of the *tessellata* complex. Unlike these species, the species of the *Cristatae* group have spurless lips. The leaf morphology, moreover, with its deeply cleft ends and broader, flatter, and thinner leaf blades, sets them apart from the type species and its allies. They are also distinguished by a propensity to produce a secondary inflorescence or even vegetative offshoot from the lower nodes of the flower spike.

The *Coerulea* Division

The leaf structure of the *Trudelia* group is much closer to the short, broad leaves of *Vanda coerulea*, itself quite divergent from the type species and its relatives. Plants of V. *pumila* are sometimes confused with immature V. *coerulea* plants in commercial shipments. The leaves of V. *coerulea*, however, are attached in a quite different manner from those of the *Trudelia* genus and from the other *Vanda* species. The leaves of typical vandas are attached to very short sheathing bracts. The point of attachment is well inside the base of the set of leaves preceding it. *Vanda coerulea* leaves, on the other hand, are attached much higher, with the point of attachment well clear of the preceding leaf axils.

Vanda coerulea is also atypical in the extremely small lip of its flowers, as well as in the length of its flower spike, its large number of flowers, and its ability on occasion to produce branched spikes. The unusual blue color, found elsewhere in the group only in V. *coerulescens* and in the lip of V. *tessellata* (where it might possibly be the result of introgression through the natural hybrid V. ×*amoena*) (Plate 2-2), also sets V. *coerulea* apart.

The *Testacea* Division

Like *Vanda coerulea*, the species in the V. *testacea* complex—V. *testacea* (Plates 2-3 and 2-4), V. *lilacina* (Plates 2-5 and 2-6), and V. *coerulescens* (Plate 2-7)—have atypically small lips relative to their sepals and petals. The shape of the petals and dorsal sepals is also distinctive, being slightly narrowed at the base, as opposed to clawed, and not being distinctly broader at the distal end. The exceptionally long erect spikes, sometimes reaching up to 3 ft (1 m), the numerous flowers, and the unusual colors set this group apart and perhaps closer to the genus *Ascocentrum*. They resemble that genus also in their foliage, which is harder and more deeply furrowed than that of the typical *Vanda*. *Vanda lamellata* (Plate 2-8) and its varieties share many of the characteristics of this group and are somewhat intermediate between these species and those of the V. *tessellata* group.

The *Spathulata* Division

Vanda spathulata is a very distinctive entity. The unique growth habit, which produces tall, vinelike plants, is quite different from the

V. tessellata group. The leaves end in unequal lobes rather than the bitten-off praemorse apex typical of the *V. tessellata* group. The spurred lip is structurally similar to that of true vandas, but the petals and sepals lack the clawed bases of typical vandas. The chromosome count is markedly different from that of the *V. tessellata* group. This quality and its habit of opening its flowers in succession over a long period rather than all within a few days both place it closer to the *Papilionanthe* than to *Vanda*. Like that genus, its habitat is in low brush, where it grows as a scrambling vine. Like many vines, *V. spathulata* requires full sun to bloom. This is very unlike the typical vandas, which are epiphytes or, rarely, lithophytes of bright but shaded locales. Its breeding characteristics are also similar to those of *Papilionanthe*. Eric Christenson is certainly correct in creating a new genus, *Taprobanea*, for this highly unusual species.

The *Tessellata* Division

The group to which the type species *Vanda tessellata* belongs is much the largest, containing about 30 species. Although much variation exists in such a diverse group of species, all share many distinctive characteristics with *V. tessellata*. Without exception, all have broad, fleshy, or leathery leaves with praemorse ends that at first glance appear to have been bitten or torn off. This quality is shared by the species in *Euanthe*, the *V. cristata* group (*Trudelia*), the *V. testacea* group, and *V. coerulea*, but not by *V. spathulata*. All of the species associated with *V. tessellata* share the vigorous, freely elongating stem habit and the vigorous production of true aerial roots along the entire stem. The flowers have strongly clawed petals with broadly bladed distal halves and dorsal sepals that are clawed or severely narrowed at their bases. The three-lobed lips are spurred and frequently furrowed or laminated on their midlobes. The lips are usually about as long, slightly longer, or slightly shorter than the lateral sepals. Most species are fragrant, some extravagantly. Some are strongly seasonal in their blooming habits, while others bloom fairly consistently throughout the year, often with definite seasonal peaks.

Within the *Tessellata* division, certain species clearly are more closely related to one another. Considering these groups of related species together gives a more cohesive view of the subgenus as a whole. Seen in this way, the section is composed of five or six, not totally exclusive groups of species that frequently have many qualities in common within individual species in other groups.

Descriptions of Species

Vanda tessellata and Its Associated Species

Associated with *Vanda tessellata* are *V. bensonii*, *V. concolor*, *V. sub-concolor*, and *V. stangeana*. All are species with a relatively northern range in northern Thailand, Burma, Laos, Vietnam, and China, and all possess flowers that are strongly tessellated, a quality shared with certain more southerly species allied to *V. limbata* and the distinctive *V. coerulea*. Two natural hybrids with *V. coerulea* are known: *V. amoena* (*V. coerulea* × *V. tessellata*) and *V. ×charlesworthii* (*V. coerulea* × *V. bensonii*). Perhaps introgression from *V. coerulea* accounts for some of the color patterns in these species. All of the species closely related to *V. tessellata* also share brightly colored blue-to-pink lips in sharp contrast to the muted colors of their sepals and petals.

Vanda tessellata (Plate 2-11) itself has an extensive range, from Sri Lanka, through India, to Burma. The medium-sized, rather fleshy leaved plants produce erect spikes of 8–12 flowers. Numerous color forms exist. The typical color is pale yellow or cream, overlaid with blue-gray or gray-green tessellation, and a bright blue lip. Less commonly, the tessellation is pale tan and the lip a bright pink. Forms in cultivation in Thailand (Plates 2-9 and 2-10) are said to have originated in Sri Lanka, but perhaps have some influence from *V. dearei* in their background. These are larger, up to 3 in (7.5 cm), and have stronger colored and, in some clones, distinctly concolor flowers in deep blue-gray and rusty red. An *alba* form of the species also exists. Two dark purple, almost black forms (Plate 2-12) have received FCCs from the American Orchid Society. The compact growth habit of *V. tessellata* and its free-flowering nature make it an attractive greenhouse subject.

On the eastern extreme of its range, *Vanda tessellata* is replaced by *V. concolor*, once considered a variety of *V. tessellata* by J. D. Hooker. As the name implies, V. *concolor* has sepals, petals, and lip of one color—cinnamon-brown. The proposed new species V. *kwangtungensis* may well be a variety of V. *concolor* but is more likely V. *fuscoviridis*. It is seldom seen in cultivation because exportation from its habitat in southwestern China has been limited. *Vanda subconcolor*, distinguished from V. *concolor* by its narrower lip with broader sidelobes, has been described, but has not yet entered cultivation. This species appears to be close to V. *bicolor*.

Vanda bensonii is also closely related to V. *tessellata*, although its range is more southerly (the Shan States and the Tennaserim Range of Burma and Thailand). Like V. *tessellata*, V. *bensonii* is a medium-sized plant. It is distinct from V. *tessellata* in several ways. Firstly, the flower spike is much longer, the flowers more numerous and spaced further apart—a quality it shares with V. *liouvillei*. The tessellated flowers are typically a dark chestnut-brown with less distinct tessellation than in V. *tessellata*. Unlike V. *tessellata*, V. *bensonii* has an even, pale rosy violet color on the outer surfaces of the sepals and petals, very reminiscent of *Vandopsis lissochiloides*. The lip, like that of V. *tessellata*, presents a vivid contrast. In most forms, it is narrow and bright pink to violet. But others betray, in this respect, a marked influence from the forked lip of V. *liouvillei*, while also sharing its duller reddish brown color. The range of *Vanda bensonii* overlaps that of V. *coerulea*, and a natural hybrid, V. ×*charlesworthii*, has been recorded. The possibility of imparting *Vanda bensonii*'s long stem and rich color to its hybrid progeny has not been fully explored.

Vanda liouvillei (Plate 2-13), which Seidenfaden has established as the correct binomial for the species widely known in horticulture as V. *brunnea*, has also to some extent influenced both the V. *denisoniana* and V. *bensonii* groups. Many varieties of V. *bensonii* have lip forms resembling the narrowed midlobe and distinctive terminal lobules characteristic of V. *liouvillei*. Also like V. *bensonii*, V. *liouvillei* possesses a long, 30-in (75-cm) or more, erect flower scape, with individual flowers spaced widely apart on the stem. In most forms, the flowers are uniformly chestnut-brown in the sepals and petals, with the midlobe of the lip the same color at the tip. The base of the midlobe is purple, and the sidelobes are white with yellow tips. In some forms, a faint tessellated pattern is discernible, as in some forms of V. *bensonii*. The elongated spike and unmistakable serpent-tongue fork of the lips makes this a very distinctive and easily recognizable species.

Vanda stangeana (Plate 2-14) is an Indian and Burmese species of medium size. The 8–12 2-in (5-cm) flowers are produced on lax stems. The overall color is dull yellow heavily overlaid with red-brown. The lip varies in color from yellow to dull rose. Like *V. tessellata*, this species has small triangular sidelobes to its lips. The midlobe, however, sets it distinctly apart. As long as the sepals and with distinctive high keels, the lip is also prominently bifurcated, a quality that allies this species to the *V. denisoniana* complex. Apparently unknown or unavailable to the early *Vanda* hybridists, *V. stangeana* yielded only six hybrids registered prior to 1985 and all of these were intergeneric. The first *Vanda* hybrid of *V. stangeana* was *V.* Motes Ginger Pied (*V. stangeana* × *V. tricolor*), registered in 1989. Its distinctive color and other fine qualities of diminutive plant size and cold tolerance certainly have great potential in *Vanda* hybridization.

Vanda petersiana appears to be closely allied to *V. stangeana* and may prove to be a variety of it. *Vanda petersiana* has not been seen in cultivation.

The *Vanda denisoniana* Complex

Related to the group of species allied to *Vanda tessellata* by their growth habits, but distinctly different in the large sidelobes of their bifurcated and pandurate (fiddle-shaped) lips, *V. denisoniana* and its associated species present many unresolved (and perhaps insoluble) taxonomic problems. *Vanda denisoniana* has been long considered to have two forms: the yellow-green form and the variety *hebraica*, or the dark brown form. Seidenfaden, reexamining the literature and herbarium specimens on the Thai vandas, has discovered that the brown form of *V. denisoniana* is correctly *V. brunnea* (Plate 2-15), and that the species commonly referred to by that epithet is properly referred to *V. liouvillei*. Seidenfaden (1988) refers to *V. denisoniana* only those "plants with sepals and petals uniformly white to greenish and yellow." Seidenfaden concedes, however, that this might be an unsatisfactory solution. Rapee Sagarik and Haruyuki Kamamoto present photographs of a wide color range, from clear to totally dark brown, in what they refer to as *V. denisoniana*. Some forms of *V. denisoniana* in cultivation have spots that are so minute as to be barely or not at all visible. These forms, when bred, produce numerous spotted and barred progeny.

Perhaps Seidenfaden's distinction (1988) should be accepted as the most practical. He believes that only the apparently pure green, white, or yellow forms are pure *Vanda denisoniana*. But a corollary to this should be the knowledge that widespread natural hybridization has occurred and back-crossing has thoroughly mixed the genes of the two species. Viewed as a hybrid swarm, the entire complex becomes more manageable. Numerous other concepts that are vaguely defined, such as *V. vipanii* and *V. bicolor*, can be assumed to be isolated variants of this group until definite and distinct populations are discovered. The potential influence of *V. bensonii* on this group is evident in the lavender color of the sidelobe and the narrow pandurate midlobes of some individuals of *V. brunnea*. If clear-cut natural locales for all of the color variants of this group are established, taxonomists will be in a better position to assign specific and varietal epithets to a group which, in horticulture, displays a bewildering variety of overlapping characteristics.

Vanda limbata and Its Associated Species

The more southerly species of the *Vanda tessellata* type present more difficulties, in part because they are little known in horticulture. *Vanda limbata* is the best known of these species. In some forms, it most closely resembles *V. bensonii*, with the plant being larger and the flower spike considerably shorter. The flowers of this form are rich chestnut on the sepals and petals, with a barely discernible tessellation, and have a simple lip of bright rose-lavender. This form has also been referred to as *V. furva*, and under that epithet received an award from the American Orchid Society. *Vanda furva* is now thought of as a Chinese species and referred to *V. concolor*. Another form of *V. limbata* is widely cultivated in Singapore (Plate 2-16). This form has a slightly narrower, yellow lip, but is otherwise indistinguishable from the dark forms. The sepals and petals are quite distinct. Their base color in these forms is dull yellow, overlaid with quite strong tessellation of dull red. Intermediate forms also exist, in which the red-brown tessellation is so nearly complete as to approach the more concolor forms. A species from the Celebes, *V. arcuata*, is apparently related to *V. limbata*, but has seldom if ever been in cultivation.

Vanda dearei and Its Associated Species

Another group of Indonesian species is best exemplified by *Vanda dearei*, native to Borneo and Pulu Laut, the ancestor of most yellow hybrids (see Chapter 5). All of the species in this group possess the thickened column base characteristic of *V. tricolor* and its related species (which are discussed later in this chapter). Like *V. dearei*, the species related to it are large plants with quite fragrant flowers. Closest to *V. dearei* is *V. sumatrana*, whose flowers smell of cinnamon (Plate 2-17). It differs from *V. dearei* in having 2.5-in (6.5-cm) flowers of a dull brown and with a slightly larger lip, but still carried on a stem shorter than the stout foliage. The related species *V. devoogtii*, which is yellow-brown with violet markings in petals and lip, is exceptionally rare in cultivation.

Vanda insignis, native to Timor and Alor Island, is a smaller plant with slightly longer spikes of 2.5-in (6.5-cm) flowers. The sepals and petals are red-bronze, and the exceptionally broad 0.75-in (2-cm) lip is deep rose-lavender. The parent of numerous hybrids with terete vandas, *V. insignis* has been underutilized in breeding strap-leaved hybrids where its brilliant, prominent lip would be a major addition to many bloodlines. The smaller size of *Vanda insignis* would make it a better breeder of pot plants than either *V. dearei* or *V. sumatrana*.

Vanda helvola (Plate 2-18) is another Indonesian species with a very distinctive lip. The lip is by far its most attractive feature, because of both the interesting arrowhead shape of its midlobe and its unique motile nature. The midlobe of this species (unlike all others) is hinged, permitting movement up and down. The flowers are otherwise nondescript, a concolor dull brown in most forms and in others a pale yellow. A brighter purple form occurs on Mount Kinabalu in Borneo. The exceptionally rare *V. leucostele* is said by R. Schlechter to be related to *V. helvola*, and may be merely a variety.

Vanda lindenii and Its Associated Species

Another group of Indonesian/Philippine species are allies of *Vanda lindenii* (Plates 2-19 and 2-20), formerly identified wrongly as *V. hastifera* in many horticultural specimens. R. Schlechter proposed calling this group *Deltalobus*, from the delta-shaped front lobe of the lip. All have exceptionally complex lips with various ornaments to the midlobe. *Vanda lindenii* itself has a lip that in its thickness is reminiscent of *Trichoglottis*, particularly such large-lipped species as *T. brachtiata*. *Vanda lindenii* produces 5–6 flowers on lax scapes two or three times a year. The medium-sized 2.5-in (6.5-cm) yellow flowers resemble, at first glance, an exceptionally large *V. lamellata* var. *boxalli* because of the brown markings on the lateral sepals. On closer examination, however, the markings are seen to be more elaborate broken patterns of color. *Vanda lindenii* is among the most fragrant of all vandas, exceeding even *V. dearei* in this quality. This is even more remarkable when considered in relation to the relatively smaller size of both the plant and flowers of *V. lindenii*. *Vanda scandens* is very similar, though the flowers are much smaller and a duller brown overall. The plant is quite different from all other species of *Vanda*—resembling a rather thin-leaved *Arachnis*—and in the future may find itself placed elsewhere, whether in *Arachnis* itself or in some other genus.

Many plants in cultivation labeled *Vanda scandens* or *V. hastifera* are in fact *V. lindenii*. *Vanda hastifera* itself, as seen in herbarium specimens, is a much larger plant with shorter scapes. *Vanda crassiloba* from Amboina is said to differ from *V. hastifera* in only very small details of the lip. Similarly, *V. punctata*, which was described by Ridley from a single plant discovered and observed from Wetter Island near Timor, may prove to be merely a variety of the wide-ranging *V. lindenii/hastifera* complex, which occurs in the Philippines as well as in Indonesia. *Vanda gibbsiae* is almost certainly synonymous with *V. hastifera* and has been formally described as such by Cribb. The rare yellow-brown species *V. celebica* resembles *V. lindenii* in the pattern and color of its sepals and petals, but is easily distinguished by its long, brilliant red lip. This handsome species, which could make a major contribution to *Vanda* breeding, is unfortunately virtually unknown in cultivation.

Vanda tricolor and Its Associates

Several species share qualities in common with *Vanda tricolor*, and all possess a thickened base to the column. *Vanda tricolor* itself is a quite variable species, occurring in two distinct forms. The typical form has a broad lip, and the sepals and petals are pale yellow, heavily mottled with red-brown. The second form, exemplified by the variety *V. tricolor* var. *suavis*, was long considered a separate species. In this form the lip is narrower but, like the brown type, pinched in the middle to an elongated pandurate form. The flowers of *V. tricolor* var. *suavis* are nearly pure white, with spots of vivid purple-red. Phillip Cribb (1981) states that both forms occur simultaneously in Java, growing on sugar palms. But C. A. Backer and R. C. Bakhuizen (1968) state that the range of *V. tricolor* var. *suavis* is entirely outside that of *V. tricolor*. This latter interpretation certainly seems much more likely.

Vanda luzonica was also, briefly, thought to be a variety of *V. tricolor*. The differences between these allied species, and the confusion that resulted from the early development of the hybrid *Vanda* Boschii, are discussed in Chapter 6.

Vanda foetida from Sumatra was used in some early hybrids but is also rare outside of Indonesia. It is described by Holttum (1964) as being shaped like *V. dearei*, with "sepals and petals grading from pale mauve, netted a deeper shade, at the edges to cream at the base, the lip with purplish midlobe and yellowish sidelobes; scent unpleasant."

Vanda merrillii from the Philippines is related to *V. tricolor* and *V. luzonica*. The yellow base color is heavily or, in the cultivar 'Rotor', entirely overlaid with rich red—a pattern similar to that of *V. tricolor*. Indeed, many of the forms in cultivation labeled *V. merrillii*—possibly including some of the awarded clones—are in reality *V.* Trimerrill, the hybrid between the two species. These are distinguishable from *V. merrillii* by their flowers, which are larger and held on shorter stems. They also appear more frequently and last longer than *V. merrillii*. One of the singularities of *V. merrillii* is that, despite their heavy substance and waxy appearance, the flowers are the shortest-lived of all vandas, often persisting for as little as 10–12 days.

Vanda roeblingiana, another Philippine species, has a color pattern similar to *V. merrillii* but much more in the chestnut-brown shade. The extraordinary feature of *V. roeblingiana* (Plate 2-21) is the bifurcated midlobe of its lip, each fork of which is further divided into fringed segments. This high-altitude, cool-growing species has the most elaborate lip in the genus. Natural hybrids between it and *V. merrillii* have been observed in shipments of *V. merrillii*. It possesses lobules—small additional knobs on the midlobe of its lip—which relate it to the *V. lindenii* complex.

The *Vanda* with the most southern range is *V. hindsii* (Plate 2-22), from New Guinea and northern Australia. The species has clear affinities to both *V. merrillii* and *V. roeblingiana*. Although a clear yellow form exists, *V. hindsii* is typically tan to rich reddish chestnut-brown, not dissimilar in its lacquered texture to *V. merrillii*. The lip also resembles the latter species.

Further Scrutiny of the Genus *Vanda*

Of the nearly 150 plants that have been assigned to the genus *Vanda*, those already discussed are either in cultivation or have some plausible validity. Many other plants are properly placed in other genera. Eric Christenson has done some initial work on this matter, and his "Approximate list of the genus *Vanda*" is included as Appendix B. Several species on the list have not been seen in cultivation in modern times. Those species that are dubious, or poorly defined (such as *V. bicolor, V. confusa, V. petersiana, V. scandens,* and *V. vipanii*), are discussed under the species with which they are associated. But there are also the following 19th and early 20th century concepts, which need to be examined by professional taxonomists:

> *Vanda arbuthnotianum* Kraenzl. Described in 1892 in the *Gardeners' Chronicle*. Williams's description of its thin, two-lobed leaves and narrow horizontal color pattern might lead one to suppose this to be an *Arachnis*.
> *Vanda cruenta* Lodd. A Chinese species, of which little is known beyond its locale. S. Cheng, and C. Z. Tang (1986) do not recognize this species.

> *V. drakei* Reichb.f. Described by Reichenbach, in 1886,
> in the *Gardeners' Chronicle*, and said to be from the
> Sunda Islands (the habitat of *V. dearei*).
> *Vanda flavobrunnea* Reichb.f. Described in 1886 with-
> out reference to its habitat.
> *V. saxatilis* J. J. Smith. An Indonesian species from the
> islands of Amboina, Buru, and Ceram.

Several other species may well prove to be extinct, while one species, *Vanda thwaitesii*, long thought to be already extinct, has been redis- covered. With the addition of the newly discovered and defined species *V. chlorosantha*, *V. flabellata*, and *V. javieriae*, the genus as now con- ceived contains between 45 and 50 species. As these are subjected to further botanical scrutiny, the result may well be the removal of the *V. testacea*, *V. coerulea*, and *V. spathulata* groups, in addition to the removal of the generally accepted *Euanthe sanderiana* and the probable acceptance of the concept of *Trudelia*. In all probability, *Vanda* will eventually be thought of as a genus of 40 species or even fewer.

Three

A Brief History
of
Vanda Hybridizing

No other genus of large-flowered orchids can boast the rich diversity of color and patterns displayed by modern vandas. But how did this floral kaleidoscope come into being? The wealth of hues and markings reflect the contribution of genes from numerous species, which often manifest themselves at five, six, or more generations removed from their source. That hybridists have been able to develop these qualities of color and markings in large flowers, essentially *Euanthe sanderiana* in shape and size, is a monument to the power of selective breeding. This and subsequent chapters will trace and analyze that process, yielding a fuller understanding of our modern hybrids and providing some insight into possibilities of use to future hybridists.

Early *Vanda* Crosses

Strap-leaved vandas were first bred in Europe, far away from the part of the world we now associate with these colorful tropical plants. *Vanda tricolor* and *V. coerulea*, the species favored by early European hybridists, possess a tolerance for cold that is lacking in many other *Vanda* species, most notably in *Euanthe sanderiana*. Much of the free-flowering and vegetative vigor of modern vandas can also be traced to these ancestors.

Crosses of *Vanda tricolor* and *Euanthe sanderiana*

Vanda tricolor is a robust and attractive plant, more tolerant of cooler temperatures than any other large-flowered *Vanda* save *V. coerulea*. When well grown, it will flower three or more times a year. Although its flowering season is best described as indeterminate, there are definite seasons in which these plants bloom more strongly. Early- to mid-spring is one of the periods of peak blooming activity. This is a significant factor (and not just for the North Temperate Zone commercial grower with his eyes on Easter and Mother's Day). *Vanda tricolor* blooms in spring in response to lengthening days, and though somewhat uncertain in its blooming season, behaves in large part as a long-day plant. *Euanthe sanderiana*, on the other hand, is a classic short-day plant, blooming only once in the fall-to-early-winter season on inflorescences initiated in response to the shortening days of late summer. When crossed with spring-blooming, long-day plants, it produces exceptionally free-flowering hybrids, the classic example being the ascocendas that result from crossing *E. sanderiana* and its hybrids with the long-day ascocentrums.

The effect is the same when *Euanthe sanderiana* is crossed to spring-blooming vandas such as *Vanda tricolor*. *Vanda* Tatzeri, the hybrid of *V. tricolor* and *E. sanderiana*, registered by the Prague Botanical Gardens in 1918, possesses pronounced hybrid vigor, an example of the floriferousness that makes *Vanda* hybrids so desirable. *Vanda tricolor* contributes sufficient vegetative strength to make plentiful leaf axils for numerous inflorescences. Its energy was particularly appreciated in Europe—hardly the most hospitable climate for vandas—but it was to find its true apotheosis in the tropical gardens of Hawaii and Southeast Asia.

The flowers of *Vanda* Tatzeri are intermediate between the two parents, but strongly favor *V. tricolor*, which contributes its heavy substance and more open shape as well as its distinctive spots. The color influence of *Euanthe sanderiana* is present in the lateral sepals and in the fuller sepals and petals. The *V. tricolor* contribution of color supplied a yellow background, and deepened and enriched the *E. sanderiana* browns with a red tone. This made the flowers of *V.* Tatzeri appear even more distinctive to early orchidists, who were unaware of the color of the improved, modern forms of *E. sanderiana*. The vivid color of *V.* Tatzeri contributes to the breeding lines of nearly all modern pinks and also to those of the dark purple-blues.

Vanda tricolor var. *suavis* (Plate 3-1), formerly considered a distinct species, is sufficiently different to make its separation from the typical forms understandable. Benjamin Samuel Williams (1894) called *V. tricolor* var. *suavis* "a truly magnificent species." The attitude toward it of early orchidists is reflected in his comment, "So noble and sweet a plant should find a home in every orchid collection"—an assessment that still holds true today. *Vanda tricolor* var. *suavis* produces nearly pure white flowers with vivid spots of purple-red and a distinctive two-toned purple lip. They are carried on long inflorescences of 14 or more 2.5-in (6.5-cm) flowers. The beauty of these flowers, coupled with the form's strong tendency to bloom in spring, make this variety particularly desirable to hybridists. Its wonderful fragrance (*suavis* means "sweet-smelling"), which it passes to its progeny, is also an irresistible asset.

When *Vanda tricolor* var. *suavis* was crossed with *Euanthe sanderiana*, the result was *V.* Burgeffii (Plate 3-2), registered by the Munich Botanical Gardens in 1928. Clearly, *V.* Burgeffii was an attempt to capture these qualities in a fuller flower of yet greater vigor. At its best, the flower is bright pink, heavily spotted with rich chocolate-brown. As in *V.* Tatzeri, the chocolate-brown coloring is neatly arranged in the lateral sepals, in a pattern that echoes (but does not exactly reproduce) the masking of *E. sanderiana*. The first impression of *V.* Burgeffii is of a vivid, small-flowered form of *E. sanderiana*, with the blossoms carried more elegantly on a better-arranged stem. *Vanda* Burgeffii brings the color and graceful stem of *V. tricolor* var. *suavis* into many modern hybrids.

The *Vanda coerulea* Influence in European Hybrids

Vanda coerulea (Plate 3-3) was regarded by early orchidists as the finest of the *Vanda* species. Its long scapes of large flowers and wonderful color, combined with its cold tolerance, made *V. coerulea* the premier parent of *Vanda* hybrids during the early years. When combined with *V. tricolor* and *V. tricolor* var. *suavis*, it produces long stems of intensely colored flowers. The color dominance of *V. coerulea* produces shades of distinct blue-purple in a clear polka-dot pattern contributed by the *V. tricolor* parents.

The interest of early European hybridists in *Vanda tricolor* and *V. tricolor* var. *suavis* is manifest in *V.* Gilbert Triboulet (Plate 3-4), registered in 1919 by Jean Gratiot, and in *V.* Herziana, registered by P. Herz in 1921. These hybrids combine *V. tricolor* and *V. tricolor* var. *suavis* with *V. coerulea*.

Vanda Gilbert Triboulet and *V.* Herziana are strikingly attractive, wonderfully fragrant plants that are still worth growing and even more worth recreating with new and improved forms of *V. coerulea* to yield larger, fuller, and brighter polka-dot flowers. The wealth of marvelous new hybrids of *V. coerulea* with standard large-flowered types, if crossed to *V. tricolor* var. *suavis*, might well produce modern hybrids recapturing the charm of *V.* Gilbert Triboulet and *V.* Herziana in fuller formed flowers more suited to contemporary tastes.

The most famous *Vanda coerulea* hybrid, *V.* Rothschildiana (*V. coerulea* × *Euanthe sanderiana*), was registered in 1931. In many respects, it has never been superseded. With improved strains of both *V. coerulea* and *Euanthe sanderiana* constantly being developed, *V.* Rothschildiana cultivars have shown consistent improvement. An average plant from a modern remake frequently surpasses an awarded clone of a previous generation.

There is also another, more important respect in which *Vanda* Rothschildiana remains unsurpassed. This hybrid embodies many of the very finest qualities of vandas: the brilliant color, distinctive pattern, large flowers, and long, multiflowered stem of *V. coerulea*, and the large, well-shaped flowers of *Euanthe sanderiana*. The resultant hybrid vigor permits these plants to produce as many as 50–60 5-in (13-cm) flowers.

Novices and laypeople universally proclaim these to be the most magnificent orchids they have ever seen.

The sometimes overly sophisticated orchidists to whom such blue vandas seem *passé* would do well to reevaluate *Vanda* Rothschildiana, the constantly evolving benchmark of the best in vandas. An idealized V. Rothschildiana, fuller in shape and in a full range of color, should be the objective in any breeding of standard vandas.

Vanda coerulea and V. *tricolor* were both recombined with the primary hybrids, already noted by the European hybridists of the 1920s and '30s, to produce an array of brilliantly colored pink and blue flowers, forming the basis of modern hybrids in these colors.

Tropical Hybridization and the Influence of *Vanda dearei* and *Vanda luzonica*

In the 1940s, there was a shift in the locale of *Vanda* hybridization to Hawaii and Southeast Asia, and interest increased in two additional species, V. *dearei* and V. *luzonica*. The cultivation of terete vandas—predominantly *Vanda* Miss Joachim—for use as cut flowers, was the major interest of growers in Hawaii, Singapore, and Malaysia. The cultivation and improvement of strap-leaved hybrids, however, was of minor importance in the 1940s. With attention focused on cut flowers rather than on pot plants, strap-leaved vandas (which required elaborate structures and more intricate care to produce fewer flowers) appealed less than the vigorous semi- and quarter-terete vandas that resulted from crossing them to terete vandas. In the late 1940s and '50s, there was great interest in the development of strap-leaved vandas as horticultural plants, in part for their potential as parents of cut-flower hybrids. Gradually their inherent beauty and ease of cultivation in tropical settings gained them a large following in areas where they could be easily grown. During the 1950s, strap-leaved vandas became a major horticultural genus in Hawaii. Everywhere else, however, all vandas were still considered "botanical." That attitude was to change gradually during the 1960s, and by the 1970s vandas were established as a standard type, taking prominence in show schedules and in American Orchid Society (AOS) judging. The Hawaiian enthusiasm led to interest in new lines of breeding from other species.

The yellow color and strong, pervasive, sweet scent of *Vanda dearei* stimulated its use in hybrids. The first *V. dearei* hybrid, *V.* Memoria T. Iwasaki (*V. dearei* × *V. tricolor*), was registered by T. Shimadzu of Tokyo in 1934. This heavily spotted flower, yellow overlaid with rich reddish brown, combines the two most fragrant large-flowered *Vanda* species. Primary hybrids from *V. dearei* can fill an entire greenhouse or tropical patio with their fragrance. The rich color of *V.* Memoria T. Iwasaki is in the background of many modern yellows and reds.

Interest in *Vanda dearei* as a parent did not become evident again until the mid-1940s, when a group of *V. dearei* hybrids were registered. Most of these followed the pattern of earlier breeding, and involved species other than *Euanthe sanderiana*. *Vanda* Helen Adams (*V. dearei* × *V. suavis*), registered by Ernest de Saram of Ceylon in 1944, produces sprays of 7 or 8 flowers of creamy white to apricot-orange overlaid with reddish brown dots. *Vanda* Memoria G. Tanaka (*V.* Memoria T. Iwasaki × *V. dearei*) is another heavily spotted yellow hybrid. *Vanda* Lester McCoy (*V. coerulea* × *V. dearei*), because of its intense purple flowers held well above the foliage, was considered by many early *Vanda* enthusiasts to be the finest primary hybrid after *V.* Rothschildiana. The waxy blossoms are held on a long flower stem, a legacy from *V. coerulea* that overcomes one of the chief problems of *V. dearei* hybrids—the short scape that holds the flowers half-hidden among the foliage.

Vanda Ellen Noa (*V. dearei* × *Euanthe sanderiana*), the ancestor of nearly all modern yellows, was not registered by J. K. Noa until 1946. This hybrid, which preserves the yellow color of *V. dearei* and much of the fuller shape of *E. sanderiana*, started the direct line that has culminated in the yellow hybrids of today. The development of *V.* Ellen Noa foreshadowed the direction that *Vanda* breeding was to take in the 1950s, when most Hawaiian breeding focused on creating a vivid, well-shaped flower by introducing the color of color-dominant *Vanda* species to the better-shaped, color-recessive *E. sanderiana*.

The pattern of breeding with *Vanda luzonica* parallels that of *V. dearei* in many respects. In addition to its desirable color, *V. luzonica* is floriferous, with as many as 19 blooms per stem. It carries more flowers per stem than any other large-flowered *Vanda* species except for *V. coerulea*. The first *V. luzonica* hybrids were *V.* Boschii (*V. luzonica* × *V. tricolor*) and *V.* Faustii (*V. luzonica* × *V.* Gilbert Triboulet), both made in Germany in the 1930s. *Vanda* Boschii resembles an improved *V. luzonica* but possesses a longer lip and more intense spotting because of the *V. tricolor* parent. Many clones of *V.* Boschii in South Florida and elsewhere are frequently shown under the name *V. luzonica*. Indeed, there is even one awarded plant of *V. luzonica* ('Fuchs', HCC/AOS), which has all the appearance of a *V.* Boschii hybrid. On the other hand, one awarded clone of *V.* Boschii appears indistinguishable from *V.* luzonica 'Evelyn' AM/AOS (Plate 3-5). These hybrids are, however, easily distinguishable from the scentless *V. luzonica* by their fragrance (inherited from *V. tricolor* var. *suavis*).

Vanda Faustii (*V.* Gilbert Triboulet × *V. luzonica*) is a spotted blue of some importance in blue breeding. *Vanda* Flammerolle (*V. coerulea* × *V. luzonica*), registered by Maison Henri Vacherot-Lecoufle in 1945, also produces an abundance of bright blue flowers.

In the 1940s, breeders began to see the possibility of *Vanda luzonica* as a parent of pinks. *Vanda* Manila (*V. luzonica* × *Euanthe sanderiana*), registered by the Rapella Orchid Co. in 1943, was the most influential *V. luzonica* hybrid. *Vanda* Manila demonstrates the ability of *V. luzonica* to transmit a high flower count, up to 15 or 16, and to produce flowers in which pink shades predominate. *Vanda* Joan Swearingen (*V. luzonica* × *V.* Rothschildiana), registered in 1948, is also an important ancestor of most modern pinks. Either *V.* Joan Swearingen or *V.* Bill Sutton (*V.* Manila × *E. sanderiana*), or both, contributed to the background of nearly every significant modern pink.

Hybridization of Modern Vandas

By the time *Vanda* Bill Sutton was registered by Oscar Kirsch of Honolulu in 1951, most of the primary and secondary hybrids that are ancestors of our modern hybrids had been produced. In the 1950s, the center of *Vanda* hybridization was in Hawaii, focused in the work of

Oscar Kirsch, Robert Warne, B. Tanaka, T. Ogawa, M. Miyamoto, and the Kodama Orchid Nursery, among others. These hybridists continued to produce primary and secondary hybrids involving *Vanda* species, but increasingly their efforts concentrated on imparting a fuller shape and larger size to already existing types.

The results of this relentless "*sanderiana*-ization" were gratifying. Larger, fuller flowers more nearly like *Euanthe sanderiana* were produced in a range of colors that preserved much of the richness of hues of the true *Vanda* species. (The detailed analysis of this process is the subject of subsequent chapters.) The Hawaiians succeeded, through this involved and intricate process, in recreating *E. sanderiana* in a variety of color forms that possessed considerable hybrid vigor and floriferousness.

In the 1960s the contributions of Hawaiian breeders continued apace. But that decade also saw the emergence of an entirely new center for *Vanda* hybridization: Thailand. The driving force behind this development was Rapee Sagarik, who saw that his native climate was ideally suited to *Vanda* cultivation, offering the potential for a whole new national industry. Since labor and land costs were lower in Thailand than in Hawaii and Singapore, Sagarik's vision was swiftly vindicated, and Thailand rapidly established itself as a center for cut-flower vandas. Cut-flower production gave Thai breeders vast *Vanda* populations from which to select future parents, just as it had for their counterparts in Hawaii (from where its initial stock was imported). Complex hybrids, produced in such quantities by Thai breeders, allowed for segregation of genes in the progeny. This in turn permitted new color types to be produced on a consistent basis.

Vanda Memoria Madam Pranerm (*V.* Waipuna × *V.* Eisenhower), registered by Palm Orchids in 1962, is an example of the direction *Vanda* breeding was to take in Thailand—and an example of its success. One parent, *V.* Waipuna (*V.* Ellen Noa × *V.* Rothschildiana), contributed an underpinning of *V. coerulea* qualities to a basically yellow flower. When combined with the *Euanthe sanderiana*-type flowers of *V.* Eisenhower, it produced full-formed yellow blooms with reddish markings, of heavy substance, borne on strong stems. *Vanda* Memoria Madame Pranerm is the parent of *V.* Thananchai and, hence, the ancestor of nearly all of the finest modern yellows: *V.* Amphai, *V.* Charles Goodfellow, *V.* Kultana

Gold, V. Ladda, V. Motes Butterscotch, V. Phetchaburi Gold, V. Rasri, V. Rasri Gold, V. Seeprai, V. Seethong, V. Southeast Beauty, and V. Thananchaisand, among others.

This is not surprising, considering *Vanda* Memoria Madame Pranerm's heavy *V. dearei* ancestry. What is surprising, however, is that V. Memoria Madame Pranerm is also the ancestor of many of the finest blues, purples, reds, and pinks. When crossed with V. Sun Tan (*V.* Beebe Sumner × *Euanthe sanderiana*), V. Memoria Madame Pranerm yields V. Madame Rattana, which is the parent of V. Charungraks, V. Gordon Dillon, V. King Naresuan, V. Piyaporn, V. Ponpimol, V. Robert's Delight, and V. Wirat, among many other significant blues and pinks. *Vanda* Madame Rattana is also the grand-parent of V. Faye Bennett, V. Fuchs Delight, V. Keeree's Sapphire, V. Motes Indigo, V. Robert Smith, and V. Rung Roeng, among others. The addition of the *V. tricolor* genes from V. Beebe Sumner widened the range of color patterns, and allowed for the deepening of both the pinks and the blues.

Vanda Fuchs Delight (*V.* Kasem's Delight × V. Gordon Dillon), which appears to have been made by several hybridists simultaneously in Florida and Thailand, illustrates the complex genetics of modern vandas from Thai breeding. Individual clones of both V. Gordon Dillon and V. Kasem's Delight range from dark purple to bright pink. *Vanda* Fuchs Delight 'Motes Orchids' HCC/AOS is representative of the dark *V. tricolor* influence that can be seen in V. Gordon Dillon 'Lea' AM/AOS and V. Kasem's Delight 'Tom Boykin' AM/AOS. At the other extreme, V. Fuchs Delight 'Motes's Jubilation' AM/AOS succeeds in perfecting the shape of *Euanthe sanderiana* (a flower so full that its sepals overlap) while also reproducing exactly the concolor pink and faint tessellation of the pink forms of *V. coerulea*.

Complex hybrids such as those from *Vanda* Memoria Madame Pranerm, from which selections can be made isolating specific geno-types, are characteristic of Thai breeding for the past two decades. The Thai breeders, consciously or not, used Mendelian segregation to sepa-rate out *Euanthe sanderiana* qualities in the form of colors and patterns characteristic of the other species. The degree to which many of these also conform to the goals of early breeders, in achieving full-formed flowers in a wide range of colors, is remarkable. The future of *Vanda* hybridization will involve recapturing yet more positive qualities from yet more species, by calculated line breeding to species and primary hybrids, adding other hues to the rainbow.

Plate 1-1. *Vanda spathulata*, the first species encountered by Westerners.

Plate 1-2. *Vanda insignis*, discovered in the 17th century.

Plate 1-3. *Vanda limbata*, one of the first species of *Vanda* to be discovered.

Plate 1-4. *Vanda tricolor*, the widespread Javanese species first described by Rumphius.

Plate 1-5. *Vanda tessellata*, type species of the genus.

Plate 1-6. *Vandopsis gigantea*, once considered a part of the genus *Vanda* by Lindley.

Plate 1-7. *Vandopsis lissochiloides*, placed by Lindley in his section *Fieldia*.

Plate 1-8. *Rhynchostylis gigantea*, placed by Lindley in his section *Anota*.

Plate 1-9. *Papilionanthe teres*, included by Lindley in his section *Euvanda*.

Plate 1-10. *Vanda pumila*, a Himalayan species described by J. D. Hooker in the late 19th century.

Plate 1-11. *Vanda flabellata*, the latest species proposed for the genus.

Plate 2-2. The blue color of the lip in many jungle forms of V. *tessellata*, shown here, could be introgression from V. *coerulea*.

Plate 2-1. The elaborate lip structure of V. *cristata* separates this species and its allies from typical vandas.

Plate 2-3. *Vanda testacea* is widely cultivated as V. *parviflora*.

Plate 2-4. The curved spur of V. *testacea* distinguishes this species.

Plate 2-5. *Vanda lilacina* is a nearly white form in many clones.

Plate 2-6. The straight spur of *V. lilacina* easily identifies this species.

Plate 2-7. The flowers of V. *coerulescens* are the longest spiked and most brightly colored of the *Testacea* group.

Plate 2-8. The typical form of V. *lamellata* is not as commonly seen in cultivation as its more colorful varieties.

Plate 2-9. This "Thai-cultivated" V. *tessellata* is said to be from stock originating in Sri Lanka.

Plate 2-10. The side view of this "Thai-culti-vated" V. *tessellata* shows differing lip struc-ture from wild types.

Plate 2-11. Note the lip structure in this V. *tessellata*, a northern-India type.

Plate 2-12. *Vanda tessellata* 'Mary Motes' FCC/AOS is one of the nearly black clones.

Plate 2-13. The exceptionally long spike and bifurcated lip immediately distinguish V. *liou-villei*, widely cultivated under the erroneous epithet V. *brunnea*.

Plate 2-14. *Vanda stangeana*, a Himalayan species, was unavailable to early hybridists.

Plate 2-15. *Vanda brunnea* is widely cultivated as *V. denisoniana* var. *hebraica*.

Plate 2-16. *Vanda limbata* 'Singapore' is more distinctly marked and more free-flowering than the Javanese type.

Plate 2-17. Dark brown V. *sumatrana* is closely related to V. *dearei*.

Plate 2-18. The lip of V. *helvola* is distinctive in its shape and its mobility.

Plate 2-19. *Vanda lindenii* is one of the species with lobules on the midlobe of the lip.

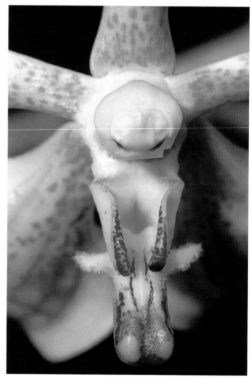

Plate 2-20. Midlip lobules are apparent in this close-up of V. *lindenii*.

Plate 2-21. The intricate midlobe of V. *roeblingiana* also possesses lobules.

Plate 2-22. *Vanda hindsii* is the most southerly of all species in the genus.

Plate 3-1. *Vanda tricolor* var. *suavis* was favored by the early hybridists for its vigor and cold tolerance.

Plate 3-2. *Vanda* Burgeffii (*V. tricolor* var. *suavis* × *Euanthe sanderiana*) is an early German hybrid that demonstrated the potential in *Vanda* hybridization.

Plate 3-3. This jungle-type *V. coerulea* is an example of the unimproved species used in the early hybrids.

Plate 3-4. *Vanda* Gilbert Triboulet (*V. tricolor* × *V. coerulea*), an early French hybrid, combines the two most cold-tolerant of the large-flowered species.

Plate 3-5. Fragrant *V. luzonica* 'Evelyn' AM/AOS is probably an exceptionally fine *V. Boschii*.

Plate 4-1. Improved forms of *Euanthe sanderiana* such as this are the results of several generations of selection in cultivation.

Plate 4-2. *Alba* forms of *E. sanderiana* are white where normally pink, and green where normally brown.

Plate 4-3. The seminal hybrid *V.* Jennie Hashimoto is a genetically improved hybrid form of *E. sanderiana*.

Plate 4-4. Richly colored and full-formed modern hybrids such as this V. Taveesuksa (V. Pimsai × V. Bhimayothin) are a perfecting of *E. sanderiana*'s best qualities.

Plate 4-5. This V. Andrew Long (V. Pimsai × V. Boonchoo) clone illustrates the pastels that result when the color of *E. sanderiana* is not fully manifest.

Plate 4-6. The masked pattern of E. *sanderiana* is evident in this V. Boonchoo × V. Gordon Dillon hybrid dominated by V. *coerulea*'s color.

Plate 4-7. Though several generations removed, V. *dearei* ancestry still dominates E. *sanderiana*'s pale pink in V. Motes Sahara.

Plate 5-1. Fragrant V. *dearei* is the ancestor of most modern yellows.

Plate 5-2. Brown forms of V. *dearei* have also influenced yellow bloodlines.

Plate 5-3. *Vanda* Memoria T. Iwasaki, an early hybrid, brought
V. *tricolor* genes to yellow hybrids.

Plate 5-4. *Vanda* Ellen Noa (*E. sanderiana* × *V.
dearei*) is a fragrant, free-flowering primary hybrid.

Plate 5-5. *Vanda* Pontip is an excellent example of a spotted yellow in full form.

Plate 5-6. *Vanda* Motes Butterscotch 'Butterscotch' AM/AOS is a concolor yellow of the type produced in the 1970s and '80s.

Plate 5-7. The clarity of color of V. Phetchaburi Gold characterizes the best of the new Thai yellows.

Plate 5-8. *Vanda* Rasri Gold is one of many fine new yellows and whites, being produced from breeding with albescent types.

Plate 5-9. Many of the new yellows, including this V. Rasri Gold, display some tessellation or masking from their E. *sanderiana* ancestry.

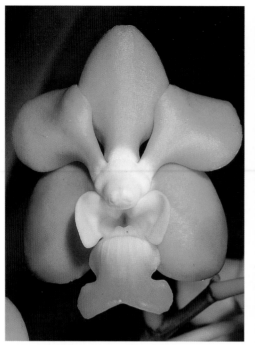

Plate 5-10. Even clear yellow forms of *V. denisoniana*, such as 'Mary Motes' AM/AOS, shown here, can often produce spotted progeny.

Plate 5-11. Most forms of *V. denisoniana* display some spots in their petals.

Plate 5-12. *Vanda* Motes Honeybun 'Golden Dawn' HCC/AOS is a full-formed, evenly spotted *V. denisoniana* hybrid.

Plate 5-13. Clear yellow progeny like this V. Motes Honeybun 'Clear Yellow' are rare but expected, and have bred pure for yellow.

Plate 6-1. *Vanda* Motes Resplendent 'Motes Orchids' HCC/AOS exhibits the rich, complex color patterns of modern pink to red vandas.

Plate 6-2. *Vanda* Motes Resplendent shows the tessellation of V. *coerulea* with the deep color of V. *luzonica*.

Plate 6-3. *Vanda* Motes Raspberry Cream (V. *luzonica* × V. *bensonii*) demonstrates the ability of V. *luzonica*'s color to dominate that of other species.

Plate 6-4. The vivid color of V. *luzonica* is quite dominant in its progeny.

Plate 6-5. *Vanda* Fuchs Delight 'Motes Jubilation' AM/AOS shows the vivid color and fullness of form of modern *Vanda* hybrids.

Plate 6-6. The upper petals of this V. Fuchs Delight 'Motes Jubilation' AM/AOS have been removed; even without them, this clone is almost without windows.

Plate 6-7. Large size and exceptionally dark color characterize V. Memoria Elizabeth Meade 'Motes Orchids' HCC/AOS.

Plate 6-8. The depth of color of V. Mitsy Shinsato 'Mary Motes' AM/AOS is greatly enhanced by its splendid texture.

Plate 6-9. The rich patterns of color of V. Chiengrai (V. Chindavat × V. Gordon Dillon) owe much to the V. *tricolor* var. *suavis* genes received from the V. Gordon Dillon parent.

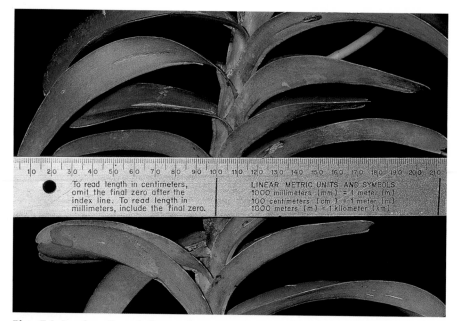

Plate 7-1. Jungle-collected clones of V. *coerulea* are much narrower than cultivated strains.

Plate 7-2. *Vanda coerulea* 'P.F.C.C.' is an exceptionally dark, full-formed clone of the Thai-improved strain.

Plate 7-3. Clear blues of great clarity of definition against white backgrounds, as seen in *V. coerulea* 'Precocious', also emerge from Thai strains.

Plate 7-4. The primary hybrid V. Rothschildiana 'Sally Roth' HCC/AOS has been continually improved as better strains of *E. sanderiana* and *V. coerulea* have been developed.

Plate 7-5. The influence of *V. tricolor* var. *suavis* is strong in V. Gordon Dillon 'Lea' AM/AOS, a popular purple clone.

Plate 7-6. Exceptionally dark clones such as V. Fuchs Delight 'Motes Orchids' HCC/AOS typically have shorter, fewer-flowered stems.

Plate 7-7. *Vanda* Motes Indigo 'Alice Blue' AM/AOS shows the full form attainable by modern *V. coerulea* hybrids.

Plate 7-8. Greater depth of color is possible in the new *V. coerulea* hybrids, such as *V.* Motes Indigo 'Indigo' HCC/AOS.

Plate 7-9. *Vanda* Danny German is a modern second-generation *V. coerulea* hybrid of large size and full form.

Plate 7-10. *Vanda* Jen Yitt × *V.* Gordon Dillon is a complex hybrid that carries *V. coerulea*'s tessellation with outstanding depth of color.

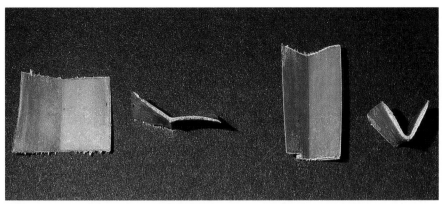

Plate 8-1. Notice the difference between the strap leaves of the *Vanda* (*V. luzonica*, left) and the V-shaped leaves of *Euanthe sanderiana*, right, which was formerly placed in the *Vanda* genus (as *V. sanderiana*).

Plate 8-2. *Vanda* Motes Raspberry Cream, a primary hybrid, shows the strong adventitious roots of true vandas.

Plate 8-3. When crossed to V. *tricolor* var. *suavis*, V. *cristata* produces vigorous, definitively colored flowers, as this V. Paki illustrates.

Plate 8-4. The pattern of color shown in V. Agatha Motes (V. *tricolor* var. *suavis* × V. *pumila*) is similar to V. Paki, but the red color is much more clearly contrasted against the pure white background from the V. *pumila* parent.

Plate 8-5. The large, strikingly two-toned lip of V. *cristata* is the dominant feature of this species.

Plate 8-6. *Ascocenda* Ann Reaben Prospero, a brilliantly marked hybrid, illustrates the continuing potential of V. *tricolor* var. *suavis* as a parent.

Plate 8-7. The newly introduced V. *luzonica* var. *immaculata* could have great breeding potential.

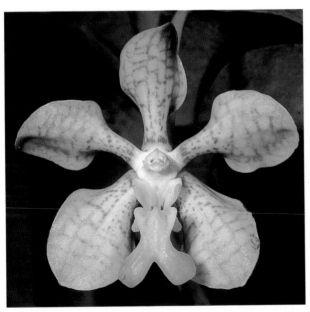

Plate 8-8. Many clones of V. *stangeana*, such as the one shown here, have very clearly tessellated yellow flowers.

Plate 8-9. Highly fragrant V. Motes Ginger Pied (V. stangeana × V. tricolor var. suavis) is the first primary hybrid from V. stangeana.

Plate 8-10. Ascocenda Rose Sutton illustrates V. stangeana's tendency to produce pink to red progeny.

Plate 8-11. Tessellated yellows such as V. Thai Checkers occasionally appear in standard lines.

Plate 8-12. *Vanda merrillii* is one of the most vividly colored species and one of the least used.

Plate 8-13. The waxy, fragrant hybrid V. Somthawil 'Bill Burke' AM/AOS blooms almost constantly.

Plate 8-14. The best qualities of V. *merrillii*— striking markings, free-flowering habit, and fragrance—are transferred to its progeny, such as this *Ascocenda* Motes Bloodstone.

Plate 8-15. *Vanda tessellata* f. *alba* may prove to be one of the most important parents of whites.

Plate 8-16. *Vanda* Thanantess exhibits delicate patterns inherited from its *V. tessellata* f. *alba* parent.

Plate 8-17. *Vanda* Mimi Palmer is a richly colored, fragrant *V. tessellata* hybrid.

Plate 8-18. *Vanda bensonii* imparts considerable spike length and depth of color to its progeny.

Plate 8-19. *Vanda* Motes Nutmeg 'Redland Spice' HCC/AOS produces numerous strikingly dark-colored flowers on long stems.

Plate 8-20. *Vanda* Kekaseh, a Singapore hybrid, is a free-flowering, bright, compact pot plant.

Plate 8-21. The flowers of V. Mellow Days 'John Ward', like those of most V. *merrillii* hybrids, possess incredible texture.

Plate 8-22. *Vanda* Singapore Sweetheart 'Mary Motes' AM/AOS is a brilliant, free-flowering new pot plant.

Plate 8-23. The subtle pastels of the best V. *lamellata* var. *remediosa* clones, such as 'Mary Motes' CHM/AOS, offer great possibilities.

Plate 8-24. *Vanda lamellata* var. *boxalli* 'Rose' AM, CCM/AOS illustrates the long stems and brilliant markings of the variety, which has been underutilized in hybridization.

Plate 8-25. *Vanda* Joan Warne, one of the few strap-leaved vandas bred from V. *insignis*, illustrates the potential of the species to contribute large lips to hybrids.

Plate 9-1. Magnesium deficiency often is revealed as reddening of the foliage in cold weather.

Plate 9-2. Both *Pythium* and *Phytophthora* molds can affect all parts of vandas. They are most devastating when infecting the crown. This view shows *Pythium* infection (black rot).

Plate 9-3. Severe drought stress causes leaves to fold closed and wrinkle.

Plate 9-4. Cuttings should be made where possible above leaves and below roots.

Plate 9-5. Wire is attached to the stem of a cutting in preparation for attachment to basket bottom.

Plate 9-6. Wire from cutting stem is attached to basket slat.

Plate 9-7. Wire cross-ties immobilize the cutting in its basket.

Plate 9-8. Thrips cause *Vanda* roots to cease growth, resulting in easily discernible rings in the roots.

Plate 9-9. The fungus *Cercospora* is easily controlled where light and air movement are adequate.

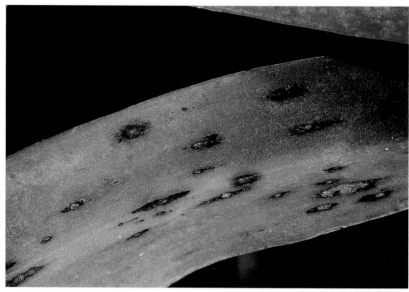

Plate 9-10. *Phyllosticata capitalensis* Henn., the "Thai disease," is cosmopolitan and easily recognized by the elongated, raised, hourglass-shaped lesions.

Plate 9-11. Southern blight, or *Sclerotium*, is a devastating disease that can be spread by air as well as water movement.

Four

Euanthe sanderiana and Its Influence

When is a *Vanda* not a *Vanda*? Perhaps when it is *Euanthe sanderiana*. First described by H. G. Reichenbach the younger in 1882, this species was referred to the genus *Vanda*. In 1914, Rudolf Schlechter created for it a separate genus, *Euanthe*. Reichenbach himself had second thoughts, and later placed his *Euanthe sanderiana* in the genus *Esmeralda*. Among modern taxonomists, Phillip Cribb of England's Royal Botanic Gardens at Kew, follows Schlechter, while Eric Christenson of Sarasota, Florida, holds to Reichenbach's first analysis.

The botanical argument centers on the structure of the lip. All undisputed species of *Vanda* have a three-lobed lip with a definite spur. *Vanda / Euanthe sanderiana* has a two-lobed lip and lacks a spur. It seems unlikely that botanical minutiae such as these would spur orchidists into a nomenclature change from *Vanda* to *Vandanthe* for hybrids. Such a change would certainly be as massive as the shift from *Cypripedium* to *Paphiopedilum*, and would also affect numerous hybrid genera. But those minutiae do, however, remind us that *E. sanderiana* and its progeny may be seen differently, depending on whether one's point of view is cultural, genetic, or aesthetic.

In horticultural terms, *Euanthe sanderiana* (Plate 4-1) differs from other *Vanda* species in several ways. Perhaps the most important difference between *E. sanderiana* and the other vandas is petal shape. This is most significant because it bears on the judging of the flowers. In *E. sanderiana*, the petals are broad at the base, whereas the other *Vanda* species have petals narrowed to a claw. Although superficially similar to other vandas, the plant also differs in two other significant areas: leaves and roots. The leaves of *E. sanderiana* are thinner and more brittle, and thus more easily broken. They are not truly strap leaves, but rather broadly and deeply V-shaped. This adaptation is due to the high light conditions of *E. sanderiana*'s equatorial habitat in the Philippine island of Mindanao, where the sunlight strikes directly on its leaves at a high angle of incidence most of the year. The leaves are set closely together on the stem with little space between, unlike the leaves of most other *Vanda* species, which are set farther apart and are much broader and flatter. *Euanthe sanderiana*'s leaf shape and carriage make it more compact but less quickly propagated. The more open leaves of true *Vanda* species are much more efficient in gathering light and the plants are therefore more rapid and vigorous in growth.

A second significant difference, related to this compact growth, is that *Euanthe sanderiana* produces roots much less frequently and bears these roots lower on the plant. This is another factor limiting vegetative propagation, as cuttings with sufficient roots are slow to develop. The leaf shape and rooting habit make *E. sanderiana* slower growing and slower to mature from seed—both of which qualities it transmits to its progeny. Leaves, roots, and the overall habit of *E. sanderiana* allow experienced growers to separate it readily from the other strap-leaved *Vanda* species.

Additional horticultural qualities also distinguish *Euanthe sanderiana* from other vandas. This species has a strong habit of blooming a single time, in fall to winter. In this habit, *E. sanderiana* differs markedly from the other large-flowered *Vanda* species, which nearly all bloom more than once a year. (One of the surest signs of the hybrid nature of many *E. sanderiana* plants in cultivation is their habit of blooming more frequently.) While *E. sanderiana* is not typical in its flowering habit, neither is it unique. Other strap-leaved species share its single, definite blooming season, among them the small-flowered group of species including *V. coerulescens*, *V. lilacina*, and *V. testacea* (placed on occasion with the ascocentrums by horticulturists). *Vanda alpina*, *V. cristata*, and *V. pumila* also share this habit, and have been proposed as a separate genus, *Trudelia*.

Cultural requirements and temperature tolerance also distinguish *Euanthe sanderiana*. Coming from Mindanao, it requires greater warmth than nearly all the other *Vanda* species and their hybrids. It is the first to react to low temperatures by ceasing growth of roots and leaves, and it is also the most likely to suffer severe damage when exposed to temperatures below 50°F (10°C) or to cold drafts at temperatures as high as 55°F (12°C). The most troublesome among hybrids are the yellows, which also have the warm-loving *V. dearei* in their ancestry. This factor, while of little importance to Thai or Hawaiian growers, should influence growers in the temperate zones. Some yellows have even been severely damaged by the air conditioning at orchid show exhibition halls.

The breeding record of *Euanthe sanderiana* provides another example of its distinctness from other vandas. Although *E. sanderiana* has been bred to nearly every conceivable attractive member of the Sarcanthinae, it frequently does so with reluctance. And when successful, it usually produces hybrids of less vigor and less fertility than those of any other similarly matched *Vanda* species.

A Desirable Parent

In general terms, there is more than enough horticultural evidence to support treating *Euanthe sanderiana* as an entity distinct from the other strap-leaved vandas. Ironically, however, horticulturists have been reluctant to do so. Some of these same distinctions have led to its predominance in hybridization since the late 1940s. As with every truly desirable species parent, *E. sanderiana* has several positive qualities. The first quality to be mentioned is the size of its flowers, in which it is rivaled only by *Vanda coerulea*. Good wild-collected clones of *Euanthe sanderiana* have produced flowers measuring 4.5 in × 5 in (11 cm × 13 cm) across, and clones appearing in cultivation from line breeding have been even larger. Because the flowers of most other *Vanda* species are considerably smaller, the flower size of *E. sanderiana* is a major factor in its frequent choice as a parent.

Flower shape is equally important, indeed possibly more so. *Euanthe sanderiana* flowers are much fuller than those of any other *Vanda* species. The sepals are exceptionally broad and full. Even more important to breeders, the petals have an entirely different shape from that of other vandas. The broad petals of *E. sanderiana* were correctly seen by early breeders as offering an opportunity to close the "windows" caused by the characteristically narrowed basal portions of the petals in other *Vanda* species.

Euanthe sanderiana flowers are not only fuller, but flatter. Other *Vanda* species generally have fairly flat sepals, but the petals can twist and turn in remarkable ways. Some reflex, and can twirl 90 or even 180 degrees. More or less flat forms can be found in superior clones, but they are the exception. The importance of the flat form of *E. sanderiana* in breeding is overwhelming.

The inflorescence of *Euanthe sanderiana* has two desirable qualities that commend it to breeders. First, it carries its flowers on an erect stem, which in the best clones tops the foliage. While several other *Vanda* species possess this valuable characteristic (*V. coerulea* even more so), *V. luzonica*, *V. dearei*, and *V. denisoniana* do not, and modern pinks and yellows would bloom almost unseen among their leaves if the influence of *E. sanderiana* did not lift up their heads.

The second highly desirable quality of the *Euanthe sanderiana* inflorescence is the even, symmetrical arrangement of the flowers on the stem. At its best, *E. sanderiana* is capable of displaying its flowers in a uniformly arranged, nearly cylindrical head. By contrast, most other *Vanda* species have a much more lax arrangement. The hybrids benefit from the fact that *E. sanderiana* is, if anything, too crowded with its flowers.

Euanthe sanderiana, while attractive, is not a show-stopper. Most unimproved forms are pale pink and are heavily masked with chocolate-brown reticulations on the lateral sepals. Whereas the actual color of the flowers may be uninspired, however, the pattern of color is very attractive. In hybrids, the two-toned effect of the marked lateral sepals is heightened, and is particularly pleasing in yellow and bright pink forms. The rather insipid base is, however, dominated by the richer color of the other *Vanda* species.

Euanthe sanderiana appears to possess several genes for the trans-mission of color. Darker forms seem to manifest a full set of strong color genes, while the *alba* forms apparently approach absolute zero. In the *alba* form of *E. sanderiana* (Plate 4-2), the normally pink parts of the flower are white, whereas all of the normally brown parts are bright apple-green. When bred to colored flowers, these so-called albas display the *E. sanderiana* propensity for incomplete color dominance, and produce blooms of a lighter shade of the colored parent. This quality of *E. sanderiana* will be thought exceedingly valuable should American orchidists again come to appreciate pastel shades as they did in the 1950s (and as Japanese orchidists and the general public do today). The path to pure white vandas also lies through *E. sanderiana* "*alba*" (see Chapter 5).

Drawbacks of *Euanthe sanderiana* as a Parent

Along with its many virtues, *Euanthe sanderiana* also transmits some of its faults to its progeny. Chief among these is its extremely strong tendency to bloom only once a year, in the autumn. Primary hybrids with other vandas usually take on the free-flowering habit of the other parent or involve long-day species, which when crossed to the short-day *E. sanderiana* produce free-flowering indeterminate hybrids. Secondary hybrids crossed back to *E. sanderiana* still manifest the frequency of flowering that was a large factor in the initial appreciation of *Vanda* hybrids. As hybrids become more dominantly *E. sanderiana* in their makeup, frequency of flowering falls off.

Many clones of complex hybrids bloom like *Euanthe sanderiana*—just once a year. Vandas that bloom infrequently have more strength, and usually produce larger, finer, and more numerous flowers. But judges, unfortunately, can judge what they see only. A plant's lack of bloom can-not be judged. Many awarded clones manifest this tendency toward infrequent blooming, as purchasers of mericlones know to their chagrin. As breeders selected for the fine qualities of *E. sanderiana*, they inadvertently were selecting for one of its negative traits as well. The solutions to this lie in the reintroduction of other *Vanda* genes to modern breeding programs, and the conscious selection of clones that flower more freely.

The slow growth rate and slow maturation of *Euanthe sanderiana* are also factors found in complex hybrids. In addition to their free-flowering qualities, early *Vanda* hybrids with less *E. sanderiana* in their ancestry possessed a further important asset: the speed with which they could be brought to bloom (4–4½ years). Compared to cattleyas, this indeed seemed rapid. But today, vandas often have the reputation of being among the slower orchids to mature—requiring up to 6, 7, or even 8 years to bloom as seedlings the size of young palm trees. This is the effect of the predominance of *E. sanderiana* in many modern hybrids. It is not uncommon to see *Vanda* seedlings entered in shows as "flowering for the first time" and topping 2 ft (60 cm)! These shy, late bloomers are exceptionally large, strong plants, and frequently produce their best blooms on this first flowering. As plants such as these receive awards and trophies, thereby encouraging their use in breeding, the trait of late blooming is being gradually reinforced in breeding lines.

Reintroduction of other *Vanda* genes will enable vandas once more to bloom in 4 years on plants 5–6 in (13–15 cm) high. One such hybrid is *Vanda* Motes Nutmeg, the result of breeding a shy-blooming *V.* Queen Kaumana to the spring-blooming *V. bensonii*, which produced flowers in just over 4 years and which blooms regularly 3 or 4 times per year. *Vanda* Kampiranda (*V.* Boonchoke × *V. denisoniana*) is another such hybrid that has proved its worth in secondary crosses. *Vanda* Thanantess (*V.* Thananchai × *V. tessellata*), although primarily conceived as an experiment in producing whites, has also introduced the precocious qualities of *V. tessellata* to yellow and white bloodlines.

Fortunately, selection for early bloom is now occurring in Thai breeding programs of standard vandas, also. Many modern grexes that show a strong *Vanda tricolor* influence in the flowers display such a precocious blooming habit that in some cases the flowering stem almost overwhelms the plant. These plants are, in some cases, so free-flowering that their full potential cannot be judged unless some of the almost constantly emerging flower spikes are pinched out.

Late-blooming and shy-blooming strains of complex hybrids are also the most cold-sensitive. These plants are frequently damaged by sudden temperature drops or are severely set back by prolonged exposure to temperatures lower than the desirable minimum of 50°F (10°C). Complex yellow hybrids of strong *Euanthe sanderiana* ancestry with the equally cold-sensitive *Vanda dearei* in their background are particularly vulnerable because they often lack any redeeming influence of V. *coerulea*. Most modern vandas have been developed in areas where cold tolerance is not a significant factor. But cold tolerance certainly is a major factor for temperate-zone growers, many of whom are attempting not only to grow their *Vanda* species in too-cold temperatures, but also, in many cases, to grow vandas that are simply too cold-sensitive.

It is clear that *Euanthe sanderiana* has contributed many of the best, and some of the worst, qualities to modern *Vanda* hybrids. The hybridists of the 1950s, '60s, and '70s were much more concerned with the virtues of E. *sanderiana*, and they did their work in truly tropical regions where its faults were either minimized or nonexistent. In Hawaii or Thailand, vandas can be grown more quickly, with no fear of cold damage, and their large size is of no significance in spacious tropical shade houses. Under these circumstances, hybridists from 1950 onward increasingly *sanderiana*-ized vandas.

Seminal Hybrids

Vanda Jennie Hashimoto and V. Mabelmae Kamahele

Prominent among these highly *sanderiana*-ized hybrids are the parents of many high-quality *Vanda* hybrids. Two grexes of this type that have had very great success are *Vanda* Jennie Hashimoto and V. Mabelmae Kamahele. Each is a hybrid with only a single non-*Euanthe sanderiana* ancestor. For all practical purposes, each is virtually indistinguishable in most clones from E. *sanderiana*. Both are exemplary of the selected and enhanced form in which E. *sanderiana* has entered modern breeding lines.

Vanda Jennie Hashimoto (Plate 4-3), registered by E. Y. Hashimoto in 1954, has the blue V. Rothschildiana as a grandparent. When crossed back to *Euanthe sanderiana*, this primary hybrid produces *V.* Onomea (G. Tani, 1948). *Vanda* Onomea clones typically come in shades of blue and pink, depending on how the recessive *E. sanderiana* genes combine with themselves or with the dominant *V. coerulea* color genes. Pink phenotypes manifesting the recessive quality are also pink genotypes. When these clones are bred back to *E. sanderiana*, the resulting *V.* Jennie Hashimoto is virtually pure *E. sanderiana* for the single quality of pink color selected. Although *V. coerulea* also contains pink genes, the oversimplification presented here is useful in understanding the process of heredity underlying modern *Vanda* hybrids.

In *Vanda* Jennie Hashimoto, breeders had a parent that possessed all the virtues of *Euanthe sanderiana*, plus heightened color, freer-flowering and longer stems, and the greater vigor stemming from the remaining *V. coerulea* genes. Selected clones even allowed for variety in color pattern. It is thus hardly surprising that *V.* Jennie Hashimoto appears in the ancestry of a large portion of modern vandas.

Vanda Mabelmae Kamahele presents a similar sequence through which positive qualities of *V. tricolor* var. *suavis* enhance the other assets of *Euanthe sanderiana*. *Vanda* Mabelmae Kamahele (*V.* Ohuohu × *E. sanderiana*, James Harvest, 1952) traces its origin to *V.* Tatzeri (*V. tricolor* var. *suavis* × *E. sanderiana*), which Herbert Shipman crossed back to *E. sanderiana* to produce *V.* Clara Shipman Fisher (registered in 1940). When crossed once more to *E. sanderiana*, this produces the very important hybrid *V.* Ohuohu. When crossed once more to *E. sanderiana*, *V.* Ohuohu produced *V.* Mabelmae Kamahele (which, like *V.* Jennie Hashimoto, is best thought of as a *E. sanderiana* enhanced by the brighter color and free-flowering habit of *V. tricolor* var. *suavis*).

The best measure of the success of *Vanda* Jennie Hashimoto and *V.* Mabelmae Kamahele is the overwhelming recognition that they and their progeny have received from the judges of the American Orchid Society. *Vanda* Jennie Hashimoto itself has received 43 awards. Seventeen grexes, of which it is the parent, also have received awards on numerous occasions. Eleven additional AOS-awarded grexes have *V.* Jennie Hashimoto as an ancestor. *Vanda* Mabelmae Kamahele has enjoyed similar success, receiving 29 AOS awards.

Vanda Jennie Hashimoto has transmitted *Euanthe sanderiana*'s best qualities to such highly awarded hybrids as *V.* Alicia Ono, *V.* Hilo

Queen, and V. Nancy Rodillas. *Vanda* Judy Miyamoto and V. Karen Ogawa, as well as V. Nancy Rodillas, owe their excellent shape and large size to the perfected qualities of *E. sanderiana*, transmitted to them via V. Mabelmae Kamahele.

By the 1960s, Hawaiian breeders could be assured of consistently breeding large, full-formed flowers of the *Euanthe sanderiana* type. The chief problem with these hybrids was that improvements in shape and size were mitigated by a distinct narrowing in the spectrum of color. Hybrids of vivid color types, produced by crossing away from the strong *E. sanderiana* influence, were inconsistent in quality. This somewhat unenviable choice between consistent familiarity or unpredictable variability inevitably led to a slowing of Hawaiian breeding activity in the late 1960s and '70s.

Vanda Lenavat and Thai Breeders

As we have already seen, interest in the breeding of vandas in Thailand began in the 1960s, when Hawaiian breeders were bringing tertiary hybrids of the *Euanthe sanderiana* type close to perfection. The vandas with which the Thais began were of this type. While continuing the development of *E. sanderiana* types, they also explored new avenues. Because of the novelty of vandas in Thailand, and the great demand for them, Thai breeders (at least during the 1960s and early '70s) found a market for hybrids that Hawaiian growers would have considered too inconsistent. Thais frequently bred secondary and tertiary hybrids together, and were thus able to select from a broader pool of the segregates.

Vanda Lenavat (V. Joan Rothsand × *Euanthe sanderiana*), registered by Phairot Lenavat in 1969, is the most influential *E. sanderiana* hybrid in Thai breeding, occupying a place comparable to that of V. Jennie Hashimoto and V. Mabelmae Kamahele in the Hawaiian breeding line. Like the Hawaiian hybrids, V. Lenavat in many clones is very similar to pure *E. sanderiana*. But, unlike the Hawaiian hybrids, it is genetically more diverse, and has the potential to produce a richer variety of patterns and colors. *Vanda* Jennie Hashimoto is ⅞ *E. sanderiana* and ⅛ V. *coerulea*, and V. Mabelmae Kamahele is ¹⁵⁄₁₆ *E. sanderiana* and ¹⁄₁₆ V. *tricolor* var. *suavis*. The percentages of V. *coerulea* and V. *tricolor* var. *suavis* are best thought of as potential maximums, because these hybrids were the result of selections for the *E. sanderiana* qualities across several generations. *Vanda* Lenavat is ¾ *E. sanderiana*, but it did not achieve this percentage by a repetitive selection for increased *E. sanderiana* qualities. Its parent, *V.* Joan Rothsand, has as its own parent *V.* Joan Swearingen (*V. luzonica* × *V.* Rothschildiana), an early hybrid outside the strict *E. sanderiana* lines. The other grandparent of *V.* Lenavat, *V.* Onomea, still bears a heavy influence from its *V. coerulea* ancestor. Indeed, *V.* Lenavat might be thought of as much like *V.* Onomea, but with a richer potential for pinks, thanks to its having *V. luzonica* in its background.

The breeding success of *Vanda* Lenavat has been outstanding. It is the parent or grandparent, or both, of 27 grexes that have received AOS recognition. Because of its complex heritage of *V. coerulea* and *V. luzonica*, it has produced both pinks and blues. Many of these, such as *V.* Bhimayothin, *V.* Boonchoo, *V.* Deva, *V.* Filipino, *V.* Fuchs Delight, *V.* Kasem's Delight, *V.* Motes Indigo, *V.* Suwapee, *V.* Varavuth, and *V.* Yen Jitt, have been very successful; more successes are expected. Most of these hybrids owe their large size and full shapes to the *Euanthe sanderiana* influence through *V.* Lenavat and to other *E. sanderiana* types. Their colors are strongly determined by the *V. coerulea*, *V. dearei*, *V. luzonica*, and *V. tricolor* genes that manifest themselves. (These hybrids are treated in detail according to their color types and genetics in subsequent chapters.)

Vanda Lenavat was also bred in the Hawaiian fashion along further *Euanthe sanderiana* lines. *Vanda* Filipino (*V.* Lenavat × *E. sanderiana*), registered by Phairot Lenavat, is a strongly colored, large *E. sanderiana* type. The clone *V.* Filipino 'Dream City' received a Highly Commended Certificate from the AOS.

One of the most successful Thai hybrids of this type is *Vanda* Bhimayothin (*V.* Lenavat × *V.* Jennie Hashimoto), four clones of which have received AOS quality awards. The consistency shown by these hybrids, as the percentage of *Euanthe sanderiana* in their background increases, lends remarkable quality. But, like the Hawaiian hybrids that preceded them, they lack variety (Plates 4-4 to 4-7).

Future Breeding with *Euanthe sanderiana*

Large, dark pink flowers with strong chocolate markings will always be appealing, even though many orchidists are relentless in their demand for novelty. Perfected *Euanthe sanderiana* types, larger and more strongly colored than any dreamed of by early hybridists, will continue to appear. Even merely average plants of hybrids such as *Vanda* Filipino and *V.* Bhimayothin are *E. sanderiana* types of a quality that exceeds the very finest awarded clones of the 1950s. The success of *V.* Joan Viggiani (*V.* Yen Jitt × *E. sanderiana*) shows that further improvements in both color and size are still possible.

These hybrids, together with the improved strains of *Euanthe sanderiana* now available, represent an open resource that will enable breeders everywhere to remake hybrids involving other *Vanda* species and primary crosses. Such primary and secondary hybrids would be as vastly improved over the originals as are modern *E. sanderiana* types over the original *E. sanderiana* cultivars. Such hybrids—larger, brighter, and fuller than the original primary and secondary hybrids—would possess superlative color and would permit access to the qualities of other *Vanda* species in a much-improved form. This would lead to complex hybrids of greater vigor and brighter colors.

The success of this approach relative to *Vanda coerulea* is evident in the continued improvement of *V.* Rothschildiana (*V. coerulea* × *Euanthe sanderiana*) or the highly successful *V.* Suwapee (*V.* Bhimayothin × *V. coerulea*). One wonders when we might expect to see new strains of *V.* Onomea, *V.* Burgeffii, *V.* Ellen Noa, or *V.* Manila?

Euanthe sanderiana (by any name) has played a glorious part in the long history of *Vanda* breeding, and promises a yet more glorious future. Still a great beauty itself, it may also breed new generations of *Vanda* hybrids that combine its virtues with those of other *Vanda* species.

Five

The Golden Heritage
of
Vanda dearei

Like the Conquistadors, *Vanda* hybridists have long been in pursuit of *El Dorado*, the golden one. The color yellow was an obvious goal in *Vanda* breeding because several *Vanda* species are predominantly yellow. Hybrids in the yellow tones were quickly and easily produced as early as the 1940s and '50s, but their perfection has yet to be achieved. As if some grudging leprechaun guarded this particular rainbow's end, yellow vandas have yet to be bred consistently to the clarity of color, perfection of form, or length of stem of the modern blues and pinks.

Vanda dearei: The Prominent Parent

Although early hybridists trifled briefly with other species (*Vanda denisoniana*, *V. insignis*, and *V. merrillii*, for example), *V. dearei* quickly became the focus of hybridists' attention because it is the largest flowered and most concolor of the yellow species (Plate 5-1). As the species most prominent in yellow breeding lines, it has contributed the most—posi-

61

tively and negatively—to modern yellows. Clones of *V. dearei* range from clear yellow to mustard to tan (Plate 5-2). The species is extremely dominant in transmitting its color, which can appear strongly in hybrids that are four, five, and even more generations removed.

There are other qualities that made *Vanda dearei* attractive. It flowers exceptionally freely, with well-grown plants blooming 3 or 4 times a year, and the flowers are outstanding in their heavy substance and their keeping quality (characteristics that are also transmitted to progeny). Then there is their quite delightful fragrance, which can flood a greenhouse or patio. Among *Vanda* species, only *V. lindenii* exceeds *V. dearei* in this marvelous characteristic, which is preserved in primary hybrids but, unlike its color, usually not beyond into its breeding lines.

Unfortunately, the ability of *Vanda dearei* to dominate its progeny for many generations holds true for its faults as well as its virtues. The open form of *V. dearei* flowers has been particularly difficult to overcome. Advanced hybrid yellows bred from this species all produce petals that are not as full as those in other color types. Some awarded hybrids still show slight windowing. Another concern for the judges' scorecards is found in *V. dearei*'s flowering habits. It carries its few (5–8) flowers in a lax fashion on short lateral stems crowded among its leaves. This sparse, short-spiked habit has yet to be completely overcome even in the most modern hybrids.

In terms of its vegetation, *Vanda dearei* is the largest of all *Vanda* species. The leaves of hybrids also tend to be longer and broader than those of other vandas. Even fifth- and sixth-generation hybrids can usually be distinguished from other vandas by an experienced eye.

The origin of *Vanda dearei* in lowland Indonesia has conferred on it an intolerance for cold that it bequeaths to its progeny. The cold-burned leaves of the yellow hybrids are always the first to reveal that a winter draft exists in the greenhouse. The size of *V. dearei*, and its intolerance to cold, make it less desirable as a progenitor of hybrids for the temperate zone than of hybrids for the tropics (where these qualities are unnoticed and unimportant).

Vanda Ellen Noa

Due to its virtues and despite its faults, *Vanda dearei* is virtually the sole source of yellow-colored *Vanda* hybrids. *Vanda* Memoria T. Iwasaki (Plate 5-3) and its hybrid, V. Memoria G. Tanaka, have exerted some influence on modern yellows, chiefly through V. Gertrude Miyamoto (*V.* Memoria G. Tanaka × *Euanthe sanderiana*) and its hybrid V. Tubtimtepya (*E. sanderiana* × V. Gertrude Miyamoto), the parent of the influential V. Thananchai. But breeding for yellow began with V. Ellen Noa (*E. sanderiana* × *V. dearei*) (Plate 5-4), registered by J. K. Noa of Honolulu, Hawaii, in 1946. Logically enough, V. Ellen Noa produced yellows of fuller shape, which were deemed more successful in the light of contemporary aesthetic standards. It is typically intermediate between its parents, with rather open, creamy yellow flowers bearing some *E. sanderiana*-like markings in the lateral sepals. Most clones of V. Ellen Noa are free-flowering and fragrant.

Although quite open in flower shape, and rather nondescript by modern standards, *Vanda* Ellen Noa was considered a very fine thing in the late 1940s and '50s. Remade with a modern, perhaps polyploid *Euanthe sanderiana*, its vigor and fragrance might even commend it to contemporary tastes. What V. Ellen Noa lacked most significantly was shape. It was therefore swiftly crossed back to *E. sanderiana*, to produce V. Eisenhower, made by the Kodama Orchid Nursery of Honolulu and registered by Yasu Funjinaga of Honolulu in 1953. *Vanda* Eisenhower was immensely successful. Fourteen AOS awards were lavished on this hybrid in the 1950s and '60s.

The *Vanda* Eisenhower Line

The *Vanda* Eisenhower line both doubled the *Euanthe sanderiana* genes and improved upon the shape of V. Ellen Noa. Perhaps more surprising, however, was the continued color influence of the V. *dearei* grandparent. Most clones of V. Eisenhower range in color from yellow to tan, bringing the color tone of V. Ellen Noa forward with little diminution, while also taking on more of the *E. sanderiana* masking. With their full, yet still open, shape, the flowers have the appearance of a fairly good *E. sanderiana* of a previous generation, but in a new color form. One notable exception is the famous clone 'Buckskin' AM/AOS, which, as its cultivar name implies, is a uniform soft tan overall.

This Mendelian segregation of almost pure *Vanda dearei* color in advanced hybrids is a quality that Thai breeders have exploited to produce consistent strains of concolor yellows. Modern yellows divide into these two classes: the *V. dearei*-dominated concolors and the *Euanthe sanderiana*-masked types.

Breeders in Hawaii and Florida continued to pursue the masked types. *Vanda* Eisensander, the result of crossing V. Eisenhower back to *Euanthe sanderiana*, was registered by Jones & Scully, Inc., of Miami, Florida, in 1962. Eight clones of this hybrid have received AOS awards. Although some are virtually indistinguishable from *E. sanderiana*, many of these third-generation hybrids preserved yellows and tawny shades from their *V. dearei* ancestor in large, full-formed flowers.

The results of crossing *Vanda* Eisenhower with the *Euanthe sanderiana*-like V. Ohuohu (*V.* Clara Shipman Fisher × *E. sanderiana*) produced V. Kaumana, registered by Takeji Ogawa of Hilo, Hawaii, in 1960. It is exemplary of the brown-toned, tessellated, *E. sanderiana* types popular in Hawaii in the 1960s and '70s. *Vanda* Kaumana, crossed in turn to *E. sanderiana*, yields V. Kaumanasand, registered by T. Orchids of Thailand in 1980. Remarkably, the clone 'Pumpkin Pie' AM/AOS preserves all of the tawny color of *V. dearei* in a flower as large and full as any *E. sanderiana* type ever seen.

Vanda Hilo Queen and Its Progeny

The most successful hybrid of these types, however, is doubtless *Vanda* Hilo Queen (*V.* Eisenhower × *V.* Jennie Hashimoto), registered by Masaya Miyao of Hilo in 1963. Ten clones of V. Hilo Queen have received AOS award recognition. This is hardly surprising in a grex resulting from the crossing of the most successful second-generation hybrids in pink and yellow. *Vanda* Hilo Queen has also proved highly successful as a parent of V. Hilo Sand, V. Lore Paul, V. Mary's Dimity, V. Papaaloa Queen, and V. Ratchada, all of which have produced clones that have earned one or more AOS awards. Most of these successful progeny are pinks, but the wonderful shape and long, strong flower stems of V. Hilo Queen still offer much to yellow breeding, although in a sense they represent the nearly complete *sanderiana*-ization of a yellow line.

Breeding the Best Modern Yellows

While yellow breeding in Florida and Hawaii was proceeding in a predictably linear direction, Thai breeders were producing hybrids that would form the basis of the best modern yellows in both the masked and the concolor *Euanthe sanderiana* types. One of the seminal hybrids was *Vanda* Memoria Madame Pranerm (*V.* Waipuna × *V.* Eisenhower), which had a profound influence on modern pinks and purples.

The *Vanda* Thananchai Line

Just as the presence of the *Vanda dearei* genes helped to make V. Memoria Madame Pranerm a superlative parent for dark pinks and purples, so the presence of V. *coerulea* genes, through V. Rothschildiana, helped to make the same plant a superlative parent of yellows. When V. Memoria Madame Pranerm was combined with V. Tubtimtepya (*Euanthe sanderiana* × V. Gertrude Miyamoto), a hybrid strongly influenced by V. *dearei* with a V. *tricolor* ancestor, the result was V. Thananchai, registered by Thananchai Sunthonwan of Thailand in 1968. *Vanda* Thananchai has been the most successful parent of yellow hybrids to date.

On paper, the genetic makeup of *Vanda* Thananchai is little different from that of V. Eisenhower. *Vanda* Thananchai is roughly ¾ *Euanthe sanderiana* and ¼ V. *dearei*, with a dash of V. *coerulea* and a hint of V. *tricolor*. What a difference there is between a sixth-generation hybrid of highly mixed parentage like V. Thananchai and a line-bred, third-generation hybrid like V. Eisenhower. Unlike V. Eisenhower, V. Thananchai carried from its V. *coerulea* ancestor a potential for longer spikes, a more erect carriage, and superior arrangement. *Vanda coerulea* influenced the size, too, of V. Thananchai's progeny. *Vanda tricolor* var. *suavis*, as an ancestral species, had a lesser but still significant impact on

V. Thananchai's progeny, while *Vanda tricolor* var. *suavis*'s stem length also helped offset the shortness of V. *dearei*'s. Its spotted color pattern has emerged to good effect in numerous hybrids from V. Thananchai. The excellent qualities of V. *coerulea* and V. *tricolor* var. *suavis* were preserved by Thai breeders in their selection of parents leading to V. Thananchai, and continued to emerge, and be valued, in its progeny.

Vanda Thananchai has been the most successful breeder of modern yellows. More than 30 AOS award-winning clones trace their ancestry to this grex. It is the parent of such successful concolors as V. Amphai and V. Rasri, and of such masked types as V. Ferdinand, V. Thananchaisand, and V. Southeast Beauty (which has received 10 AOS awards).

When crossed with *Vanda* Satta (whose parent, V. Ohuohu, also has V. *tricolor* in its background), V. Thananchai has also produced wonderfully red-spotted and mottled yellows in V. Sankamphaeng (four clones of which have received AOS recognition). *Vanda* Satta combined with the V. Thananchai parent, V. Memoria Madame Pranerm, produced V. Pontip (Plate 5-5). This was another attractively spotted hybrid, and thus part of a group that should have become an established target in *Vanda* breeding. Spotted flowers do not seem to be as favored by the Thais as concolors, but there are many others who find them very attractive. Pale background color contrasted by dark, clear counterpoint is extremely popular with American orchidists—a fact that is illustrated by the unflagging popularity of the purple and white V. Gordon Dillon 'Lea' AM/AOS. We can only hope that breeders will again pursue spotted color forms in the yellows.

As a parent, *Vanda* Thananchai has scored its most consistent and notable successes in producing the concolor yellows so prized by the Thai. Many of the most beautiful among these yellows—including V. Seeprai (V. Aurawan × V. Thananchai) and V. Seethong (V. Seeprai × V. Thananchai)—have been parented by V. Thananchai.

Vanda Rasri and Its Progeny

Perhaps the most successful plant—in terms of both its own development and its proven potential as a breeder—is *Vanda* Rasri (V. Pranerm Ornete × V. Thananchai). Created by Amnuay Sathirasut of Bangyikan Nursery in Bangkok, Thailand, V. Rasri is noted for its clarity of yellow color (which in some clones approaches green), and set a new standard for concolor yellows. It is the parent of such successful hybrids as V. Charlie Clark and V. Fuchs Sunshine. But the most successful progeny of V. Rasri is V. Kultana Gold (V. Pong Tong × V. Rasri), again created by Sathirasut. Clones of this hybrid have received 5 AOS awards. These hybrids, typically, are large, fairly full plants, uniformly mustard-colored in varying degrees of intensity. Remarkably, this is precisely the color of a typical V. *dearei*—emerging undiminished at six generations removed from its source. The color, while pleasant, is hardly arresting. More pleasing results come from the hybrid of V. Kultana Gold with V. Seeprai, registered as V. Motes Butterscotch. Most of these possess the same flat mustard-colored background. But in some clones, such as 'Butterscotch' AM/AOS (Plate 5-6), this is marvelously suffused with rose, giving a brighter, more lively effect.

Perhaps more successful in the long haul is the line pursued by Sathirasut in producing *Vanda* Seeprai and V. Seethong. A successful hybrid to emerge from these lines, V. Phetchaburi Gold (V. Kultana Gold × V. Seethong), was registered by Supote Sanimthong of Thailand in 1984. It has with some consistency produced exceptionally fine, full-formed, clear yellow-greens (Plate 5-7). This excellent color has emerged repeatedly in individual clones of various grexes, such as V. Charlie Clark 'Brandi' AM/AOS. The clarity of these yellow-greens is much more striking than the dull mustard colors of too many hybrids. As parents are selected for this desirable quality, one hopes to see more stable lines of finer colored, truer concolor yellows. *Vanda* Phetchaburi Gold may well prove just the beginning.

Another exceptionally promising new direction in yellows has developed with the introduction of *Vanda* Rasri Gold (V. Thananchaisand × V. Kultana Gold) (Plate 5-8). Sathirasut again has bred along V. Thananchai lines to produce fine yellows of the masked type (Plate 5-9).

A "White" Vanda

Yellows were the dominant product of the cross of *Vanda* Thananchaisand and *V.* Kultana Gold, but numerous albescent forms also have emerged. These resemble *Euanthe sanderiana* var. *alba* in color, with varying degrees of green to pale yellow markings on a pure white background. These *alba* types, unlike the inbred *E. sanderiana* var. *alba* clones, often possess great vigor, and bloom 2 to 3 times per year. Their breeding potential is immense: because the patterning of green color occurs in various and different places on the flower, these plants may be able to produce pure white. Sibling crossings may produce a few completely white clones. Such crosses have been made in Thailand and in Florida, as have crosses to *E. sanderiana* var. *alba*.

Both efforts were intended to intensify and concentrate the superlative qualities of these clones. Bred back to green-yellows of the *Vanda* Phetchaburi Gold type, which might be thought of as exhibiting an alba form of *V. dearei* color, clear yellows and pale greens to whites of fine shape could emerge. These albescent *V.* Rasri Gold clones, because of the *Euanthe sanderiana* quality of incomplete dominance for color, have the potential to breed pastel shades of blues and pinks, should the popularity of dark colors decline. *Vanda* Rasri Gold and *V.* Phetchaburi Gold are exciting because of the different ways in which they overcome, in part, the greatest problem in yellows bred from *V. dearei*—the persistent recurrence of the dull mustard-brown color in these hybrids.

Vanda denisoniana and Its Hybrids

There is, however, still one more path to yellow vandas, and it is a path that may also lead us to the solution to the color problem. It leads via *Vanda denisoniana*, whose flowers are a clear, bright yellow, often verging on green (Plate 5-10). This color, unfortunately, exists only at one end of the species' spectrum. On close examination, forms that appear clear yellow frequently possess minute spots of reddish brown (Plate 5-11). In some forms, these spots are quite obvious: they are, for example, large and prominent in the variety *hebraica*, resembling alphabetic forms. In others, the brown color predominates. This spotting presents great difficulty if one is seeking clear concolor yellow. Many hybrids made from *V. denisoniana* have disappointed because what appeared to be a totally clear form gave heavily marked progeny. If one finds marked flowers attractive, this disadvantage obviously becomes a virtue.

Vanda denisoniana possesses other advantages as well. It has a larger, more erect inflorescence that produces more flowers than *V. dearei* (*V. denisoniana* can produce up to 12 flowers) and also presents those blooms more attractively. Although not quite as free-flowering as *V. dearei*, *V. denisoniana* will flower two or more times a year when grown well. Its primary blooming season in spring makes it an ideal mate for fall-blooming *Euanthe sanderiana* types, a combination that produces free-flowering hybrids. The tendency of its hybrids to bloom around Mother's Day is hardly a disadvantage for the American market, either.

The plant size of *Vanda denisoniana* is considerably smaller than that of *V. dearei*, and hybrids from it tend to be more precocious. A further advantage of *V. denisoniana* is its cold resistance, thanks to its origin in the Arrakan Mountains of Burma at elevations of 2000–2500 ft (610–762 m) above sea level. Smaller size and cold hardiness should make hybrids from *V. denisoniana* more attractive to greenhouse-bound growers than hybrids from *V. dearei*.

One might suspect that a native species such as *Vanda denisoniana* would have been exploited fully by the Thai. The initial results of using *V. denisoniana* with parents from hybrids bred in the 1950s were, however, disappointing. Consequently, few hybrids from *V. denisoniana* were registered in the 1960s and '70s. With the advent of modern, consistently full-formed hybrids, the prospects for breeding with *V. denisoniana* are greatly enhanced. Not only is *V. denisoniana* frequently better shaped than *V. dearei*, it also gives spectacular results when crossed to hybrids five or six generations removed from the *Euanthe sanderiana* cultivars that made the original *V.* Ellen Noa clones.

An example of this is *V.* Motes Honeybun, a hybrid of *Vanda denisoniana* with *V.* Kultana Gold. Compared to modern yellow hybrids, these do not dazzle in size or shape. But in comparison to the original *V. dearei* primary hybrid, V. Ellen Noa, they are sensational. The flowers are often as large as V. Ellen Noa, and as a group are vastly superior to that grex in shape. The best have petals broad enough to close the "windows" between sepals and petals. Though the shape of these flowers impresses only in comparison to the primary V. *dearei* hybrids, their color impresses unequivocally. The awarded clone 'Golden Dawn' is pale gold overall and uniformly and evenly marked with pointillist spots of golden brown (Plate 5-12). Other clones have larger spots on yellow backgrounds. But most exciting are the several clones that have marvelous clarity of bright yellow, clearer and more undiluted than has ever been seen before in hybrid vandas (Plate 5-13).

These intense true yellows, when bred to the best yellows from the *Vanda dearei* breeding line emerging in such hybrids as V. Phetchaburi Gold, and to the best of the full-formed "almost *albas*" of the V. Rasri Gold type, should produce a new generation of true pure yellows. At last, perhaps, orchidists can wring true gold from the mischievous leprechaun at the end of this rainbow.

Six

Unraveling a Rainbow: Our Modern Pink Hybrids

We have become accustomed to the bright, shocking, almost-red pinks of modern hybrid vandas. While *Vanda* species certainly display those colors, they do not do so in the depth and variety found in current hybrids. These pinks are extremely complex hybrids that combine color and pattern from species far removed, in ways that intensify the effects of each. This is more remarkable because pink color in vandas is recessive to blue and, to a degree, yellow and brown. This recessive element and the sheer complexity of modern pink hybrids are the two principal reasons why the plants are so spectacular when successful. But they are also the reasons why, in many grexes, so few individual clones succeed.

An Examination of Color Patterns

Many modern pink vandas combine all the color patterns contributed by the four species that together have produced these complex hybrids. Without genes from *Euanthe sanderiana*, *Vanda coerulea*, *V. tri-*

color, and *V. luzonica*, the complexity of color and pattern in modern hybrids could not have come to be. Flowers such as *V.* Deva 'Robert' and *V.* Motes Resplendent 'Motes Orchids' HCC/AOS (Plate 6-1) display this heritage. Five or more distinct color patterns make up the total effect in the latter clone. The lateral sepals are darkest, bearing an almost solid mask of color. Some of this color reveals a reticulate or tessellated pattern, which also can be discerned on the petals and dorsal sepals. A band of rich, dark color appears at the base of the sepals and petals surrounding the column. The color is darkest toward the ends of the sepals and petals, fading at the very edges. The petals and dorsal sepal are spotted with darker color. The lighter areas of the flower between the spots are all overlaid with a rosy suffusion. Each of these color patterns is traceable to the ancestral species from which modern pinks were developed.

Masking: The Influence of *Euanthe sanderiana*

The *Euanthe sanderiana* masking is an obvious contribution to many pinks, even though its own mask is chocolate-brown. *Euanthe sanderiana* is able to transmit its masked pattern without this color in both pinks and blues, usually as an overall intensification of color in the lateral sepals. This is probably the effect of *crossover*, in which normally linked qualities are separated by the movement of genetic material from one chromosome to another during meiosis. In plants such as orchids, which produce immense numbers of progeny, this can be a fairly common occurrence. *Euanthe sanderiana's* masking is a major contribution because the lateral sepals of vandas are the largest of its flower parts.

Tessellation: The Influence of *Vanda coerulea*

The tessellated pattern in many pink vandas is the heritage of *Vanda coerulea* in one of its recessive modes. Such tessellated patterns in basically concolor pink flowers create some of the most attractive of modern vandas (Plate 6-2). The vibrant pink is as clearly tessellated as in *V. coerulea*. Since pink forms of *V. coerulea* are known to occur in nature, both self-pollination and sibling-crossing in primary *V. coerulea* hybrids consistently produce many pinks of the *V. coerulea* type. Pink tessellation is a recessive characteristic that has become a more consistently stable influence in modern pink breeding lines.

The other color attributes noted in modern pink hybrids—barring of the sepals and petals around the column and at their ends, spotting, and the overlay of rosy color—owe their genesis to *Vanda tricolor* var. *suavis* and *V. luzonica.*

Spots or Dots: The Influence of *Vanda tricolor*

The dark form of *Vanda tricolor* influences the production of the deep purple, heavily marked flowers that we associate with *V. Kasem's Delight* (see Chapter 7). Pinks of the type of *V. Motes Resplendent* are in essence the same type of flower as these purples, in another color. Breeding for dark purples almost always produces significant numbers of clones in which the recessive pink color manifests itself. In part, this is the influence of the pink phases of *V. tricolor* var. *suavis*, as is evident in the multitude of spots.

Bars or Streaks: The Influence of *Vanda luzonica*

Vanda luzonica's pink can dominate even the strong brown color of such species as *V. bensonii* (Plate 6-3). In breeding for clear pink shades, *V. luzonica* is even more evident. Once considered a variety of *V. tricolor*, *V. luzonica* differs from *V. tricolor* var. *suavis* in several respects. While both have pale flowers marked with bright pink, the color of *V. tricolor* var. *suavis* is in spots or dots, whereas that of *V. luzonica* is in bars or streaks (Plate 6-4).

The distribution of color also differs. *Vanda luzonica* concentrates its color at the margins of the flower—frequently carrying color to the very ends of the sepals and petals—and has a distinct ring of solid color at the base of the sepals and petals. The spots of *V. tricolor* are concentrated toward the middle of the sepals and petals, and the color fades at the edges into the pale outline or picotte inherited by most modern dark purples and by many dark pinks. The lips also differ in color and shape: that of *V. luzonica* is shorter and concolor magenta, whereas that of *V. tricolor* is longer, with a distinctly lighter patch toward the tip.

Breeding Lines of Modern Pink Vandas

When *Vanda tricolor* and *V. luzonica* are crossed, the resulting hybrid, *V.* Boschii, carries both patterns. This hybrid was introduced to cultivation at virtually the same time as *V. luzonica*, resulting in much horticultural confusion. The plant awarded as *V. luzonica* 'Fuchs' HCC/AOS reveals the color patterns of both species, making an exceptionally beautiful flower but one that is almost certainly not pure *V. luzonica*. Further confusion has resulted from the new identity of the awarded *V.* Boschii 'Nishida Orchids', which appears to be almost identical to *V. luzonica* 'Evelyn' AM/AOS. A third awarded clone, *V. luzonica* 'Lone Star' HCC/AOS, is also a definite hybrid. Highly regarded in the 1930s and '40s, hybrids of this type are regaining popularity in more modern forms, as exemplified by the two awards to *V.* Mary's Dimity (the result of crossing *V.* Monacensis, an early *V. tricolor* hybrid, with a modern full-formed *V.* Hilo Queen).

The *Vanda* Manila Line

Vanda luzonica's contribution of intense color and distinctive patterns to modern pink hybrids is a further illustration of the profound effects that can be achieved through selective breeding and Mendelian segregation. Numerically and theoretically, *V. luzonica* represents only $\frac{1}{20}$ of the parentage of *V.* Motes Resplendent. Yet its qualities are clearly discernible six generations removed from the species. *Vanda* Motes Resplendent received its *V. luzonica* genes from both parents. This line of breeding began in the 1940s with *V.* Manila (*Euanthe sanderiana* × *V. luzonica*), registered by the Rapella Orchid Co. of Hawthorne, California, in 1943, but later remade in both Hawaii and Singapore. *Vanda* Manila was a hit. Its *V. luzonica* parent produced bright pink colors and longer inflorescences with more flowers. (*Vanda luzonica* is capable of carrying up to 20 flowers per inflorescence.)

Crossed back to *Euanthe sanderiana*, *Vanda* Manila begat the esteemed *V.* Bill Sutton, a very bright pink, full-formed *E. sanderiana* type. This, in turn, when bred to *V. coerulea*, produced the successful *V.* Hilo Blue. The excellent pink *V.* Diane Ogawa resulted from crossing *V.* Hilo Blue again to *E. sanderiana*. *Vanda* Diana Ogawa crossed to

V. James Toogood (*V.* Waipuna × *E. sanderiana*) yielded *V.* Patou, which, when bred with *V.* Lenavat, produced *V.* Pimsai. Many modern pink hybrids, such as V. Pimsai, owe much of their intensity to the influence of *V. luzonica* carried through several generations of Hawaiian breeding and two generations of Thai breeding.

Breeding lines through V. Bill Sutton and V. Diane Ogawa are important. But they pale beside the influence of *V. luzonica* created in Thai breeding lines.

The Lenavat Hybrids

Modern pink hybrids gained much more from *Vanda luzonica* through the work of Phairot Lenavat, who in 1969 registered V. Lenavat (*V.* Joan Rothsand × *Euanthe sanderiana*). *Vanda* Joan Rothsand (registered by P. Lenavat in 1964) is a secondary *V. luzonica* hybrid resulting from the crossing of V. Joan Swearingen with V. Onomea. Lenavat's objective was probably to produce full-formed flowers of the intense violet type of *V.* Joan Swearingen (*V. luzonica* × *V.* Rothschildiana), which was itself an early attempt to produce fuller-formed flowers of the vivid but open-formed V. Flammerolle (*V. coerulea* × *V. luzonica*) type. Although V. Joan Rothsand has influenced dark purple breeding—a prominent example being V. Varai Sun (*V.* Joan Rothsand × *V.* Sarojini)—the interesting and slightly ironic result of this line of breeding was to produce the parents of the very finest pinks.

Vanda Lenavat, by almost any criteria, is the most successful parent of pink vandas. Although only one clone of this hybrid has received recognition from the American Orchid Society, 30 grexes that have won awards from the AOS have V. Lenavat as a parent or an ancestor. These 30 hybrids have, to date, received 51 quality awards.

The happy combination of *Vanda luzonica*, *V. coerulea*, and *Euanthe sanderiana* in V. Lenavat has contributed to such fine masked *E. sanderiana*-type pinks as V. Arnothai, V. Bhimayothin, and V. Boonchoo, as well as blues and purples such as V. Kasem's Delight, V. Motes Indigo, and some strains of V. Fuchs Delight (see Chapter 7).

The greatest contribution of *Vanda* Lenavat is to the pink breeding lines of such modern hybrids as V. Deva, V. Kasem's Delight, V. Sumnon Sophonsiri, V. Yen Jitt, and some strains of V. Fuchs Delight.

The success of *V.* Lenavat's *Vanda luzonica*-dominated influence in pink hybrids is most graphically illustrated in the lines emanating from *V.* Thospol (*V.* Lenavat × *V.* Rothschildiana). In addition to being the parent of the highly regarded *V.* Yen Jitt, *V.* Thospol was a parent of *V.* Deva, which was registered by Charungraks Devahasdin in 1979. *Vanda* Deva can produce dark, spotted purples, as in the clone 'Orchidgrove' AM/AOS. But the beautiful clone 'Robert' AM/AOS illustrates the intensity of pink to red color resulting when the *V. luzonica* influence predominates. The wonderful richness of this clone's raspberry-purple color (ultimately originating in *V. luzonica*) captured the Grand Champion award at the Eleventh World Orchid Conference in Miami in 1984.

The *Vanda* Kasem's Delight Hybrids

A second hybrid registered by Lenavat, *Vanda* Sun Tan (*V.* Beebe Sumner × *Euanthe sanderiana*), has also had an immense influence on modern pinks. *Vanda* Sun Tan introduced *V. tricolor* genes from its ancestor *V.* Tatzeri (*E. sanderiana* × *V. tricolor*), parent of *V.* Clara Shipman Fisher and grandparent of *V.* Beebe Sumner, to modern *Vanda* bloodlines. The intensity of color from *V. tricolor* is evident in the rich crimson of *V.* Madame Rattana (*V.* Sun Tan × *V.* Memoria Madame Pranerm). This important hybrid is the parent of *V.* Gordon Dillon as well as of numerous other successful modern pinks, such as *V.* Charungraks, *V.* Pattaya Beach, *V.* Piyaporn, *V.* Plum Red Delight, *V.* Richard Peterson, and *V.* Robert's Delight.

Vanda Sun Tan crossed with *V.* Thospol produced *V.* Kasem's Delight. Through *V.* Thospol, *V. tricolor* var. *suavis* has had an influence on modern dark pink to red hybrids by way of *V.* Kasem's Delight, much like the influence of the dark forms of *V. tricolor* on modern purples. *Vanda tricolor* var. *suavis* has contributed much of the depth of color in the rich magenta shades of modern hybrids.

Vanda Kasem's Delight (*V.* Thospol × *V.* Sun Tan) has proved itself an even more successful parent of bright pinks. However, in its pink progeny, *V.* Kasem's Delight tends to manifest more of its *V. luzonica* ancestry, particularly when paired with hybrids that share *V. luzonica* in their backgrounds.

Vanda Fuchs Delight (*V.* Kasem's Delight × *V.* Gordon Dillon) comes to mind first when one thinks of *V.* Kasem's Delight hybrids. Numerous strains were bred from this hybrid, which originated in Thailand. Many were bred with blue to purple clones of both parents, and many were bred with pinks. *Vanda* Fuchs Delight 'Motes Jubilation' AM/AOS (Plate 6-5) exemplifies the best of these new hybrids. At first bloom (the stage at which it received its award), the flowers were not only exceptionally large but incredibly full-formed. Not only did the petals overlap the sepals, but the sepals themselves overlapped one another. Even with the petals removed, the flower shows less windowing than some awarded pinks of a previous generation (Plate 6-6). 'Motes Jubilation' holds its numerous flowers well on an erect inflorescence. The color is bright *V. luzonica* pink, clearly pronounced in definite tessellation. This clone, fuller in form and larger in size than the best *Euanthe sanderiana*, carries the color and patterning of two of its distinct *Vanda* ancestors—remarkable testimony to the power of selective breeding.

When crossed to its half sibling, *V.* Madame Rattana, by Som Porn of Nakonsawan, Thailand, *Vanda* Kasem's Delight has produced full-formed, deeply crimson flowers in *V.* Robert's Delight. Breeding along the same lines also produced excellent results from another half-sibling of *V.* Kasem's Delight, *V.* Yen Jitt (*V.* Thospol × *V.* Jennie Hashimoto). Crossed with *V.* Phairot, it produced *V.* Memoria Elizabeth Meade 'Motes Orchids' HCC/AOS (Plate 6-7). The exceptionally large and numerous flowers of this clone are carried on long stems. Although the form is less than full, the vivid electric pink (from its *V. luzonica* ancestry) is overwhelming. The influence of *V. coerulea* is still discernible in the underlying tessellation of this otherwise concolor flower.

When Thai breeders crossed V. Yen Jitt to V. Bangkok Blue (the blue parent of V. Gordon Dillon), the results were equally impressive. *Vanda* Mitsy Shinsato 'Mary Motes' AM/AOS (Plate 6-8) is flat and fully formed. The flowers are carried on long stems well above the plants. The more direct influence of *V. coerulea* in its ancestry gives this clone a much deeper shade of burgundy and adds an underlay of tessellation to the predominantly concolor pattern. The rich texture of this clone, difficult to capture in a photograph, adds depth to its color and was a prime factor in its receiving the high score of 86 points in award judging.

Thai breeders have continued to use *Vanda* Gordon Dillon itself in breeding pinks, with excellent results. Crossed with V. Chindavat (*V.* Lenavat × *V.* Sunray), it has produced large-flowered pinks with fascinating patterns. The illustrated clone of V. Chiengrai (Plate 6-9) is both fuller-formed and larger than V. Gordon Dillon. Like its parent, this clone and many of its siblings have clear, precise markings over a very pale base color. Indeed, if it were not for the *Euanthe sanderiana* masking in the lateral sepals, this flower might be thought of as a perfected V. *tricolor* var. *suavis*.

Flowers with distinct markings on a pale background, such as these forms of *Vanda* Chiengrai and the large-flowered clone of V. Gordon Dillon 'Lea' AM/AOS, are perennially popular. Other successful pinks, such as V. Dona Roma Sanchez (V. Faye Bennett × V. Kasem's Delight) and V. Kretcant (V. Gordon Dillon × V. Boonchoo) continue to emerge from Thai breeding. Clearly tessellated patterns, such as those evident in V. Fuchs Delight 'Motes Jubilation' and in the illustrated clone of V. Motes Resplendent (Plate 6-1), are also a worthwhile standard in pink *Vanda* breeding. More complex color patterns like that of V. Motes Resplendent 'Motes Orchids' and V. Deva are more difficult to achieve in a consistent manner. As breeding along these lines continues, new and exciting varieties can be expected to emerge.

Seven

Vanda coerulea and the Blues

Blue, the rarest color in flowers, is rarer yet in orchids. So-called blue cattleyas are a conventional classification, not a reality. *Zygopetalum* lips, and those of *Acacallis cyanea*, are actually blue-violet. True sky-blue exists in cultivated orchids only in the flowers of *Vanda coerulea*.

The early hybridists saw in *Vanda coerulea* much more dynamic potential than in the large, formal, and rather staid *Euanthe sanderiana*. Measured by the eye of the beholder rather than the orchid judge's ruler and score card, *E. sanderiana* is humbled and overwhelmed by the profusion of open, loosely arranged, stunning blue flowers on long scapes produced by *V. coerulea*.

Vanda coerulea is found throughout the Himalayas, ranging from India and Nepal to Burma, northern Thailand, and southern China. It grows at elevations ranging from 2500 ft (762 m) to a maximum 4000 ft (1219 m), at which point the plants are subjected to night temperatures that are considerably lower than those experienced by most other *Vanda* species. *Vanda coerulea* cannot be maintained for very long at sea level in the true tropics, and inexperienced growers in subtropical areas frequently complain that it is an orchid difficult or impossible to grow. This cold tolerance, one of the factors that endeared the species to early European breeders, continues to be significant for growers of vandas in the temperate zone.

Vanda coerulea plants can become rather tall, growing to 6 ft (2 m) or more, and this is a characteristic that should be noted by those whose climate forces them to grow vandas in greenhouses. The leaf span of *V. coerulea* is quite narrow, however, occupying much less bench space than *Euanthe sanderiana*. As for jungle plants of *V. coerulea*, although some specimens can be 9 in (22 cm) or slightly more, many are scarcely more than 6 in (15 cm) across (Plate 7-1). Cultivated forms originating in Thailand are frequently 2–2½ times as broad. Whether this is the result of polyploidy (i.e., an additional set or sets of chromosomes), or whether it indicates a hybrid nature, must be left to conjecture. Some tetraploid individuals (plants with two complete sets of chromosomes) have been confirmed in some Thai seedling populations, but all the cultivated forms are improvements over the wild forms, in terms of their color and shape (Plate 7-2). Many overcome the *V. coerulea* tendency to twist its petals a full 180 degrees.

Vanda coerulea as Parent

As a breeding plant, *Vanda coerulea* has contributed just as many positive features to modern vandas as *Euanthe sanderiana* has, and many more than any other *Vanda* species. *Vanda coerulea* has given size, floriferousness, vigor, cold tolerance, color pattern, and length of inflorescence to its hybrids. Its open shape, with windows between petals and sepals, is quickly overcome in second and third generations, and its other positive characteristics appear in nearly all modern *Vanda* hybrids, including some of the best yellows.

The most striking feature of *Vanda coerulea* is, without doubt, its range of colors. There are blue flowers of course, but this orchid also occurs in shades ranging from pure white (seen in Chiengmai, Thailand) through pinks to almost reds, to blues, intense lavenders, and purples. The influence of *V. coerulea* as a pink parent is less well-known, but pink *V. Rothschildiana* (*Euanthe sanderiana* × *V. coerulea*) clones are not that uncommon, and frequently appear in seedlings from self-pollination and sibling crossings. (See Chapter 5 for more on pink vandas.)

Apart from its range of colors, *Vanda coerulea* also contributes to its progeny its overall tessellated color pattern. This marking, which it possesses in common with some other Himalayan species (*V. bensonii*, *V. stangeana*, and *V. tessellata*), is subdued in most jungle-collected plants, appearing as a faint pattern that can be read through the blue base color. In hybrids, the pattern emerges with authority and clarity, producing flowers boldly marked with a regular network of darker lines bordered by a nearly white coloration. This patterning is also characteristic of the cultivated forms of *V. coerulea* that have appeared in Thailand (Plate 7-3). In secondary and tertiary hybrids, the pattern is frequently muted, but can reappear in a subtle way at several generations removed from the *V. coerulea* ancestor.

The inflorescence of *Vanda coerulea* has also made a significant impact on modern hybrids. It is both long and erect, sometimes as long as 2 ft (60 cm), with two or more branches that can carry up to 25 flowers. The inflorescence is held well above the foliage, with the first flowers opening quite clear of the leaves. *Vanda coerulea* also spaces its flowers in a less crowded way. The long, cylindrical flower heads of modern vandas gain their height and spacing from *V. coerulea* and gain their symmetrical arrangement nearly as much from *V. coerulea* as from *Euanthe sanderiana*.

As luck would have it, *Vanda coerulea*, in addition to its other virtues, is the most free-flowering *Vanda* species. Well-grown plants will flower 3, 4, or even 5 times a year, and *Vanda coerulea* also transmits this quality to its progeny. Primary hybrids are often as free-flowering as *V. coerulea*, and tend to extend their flowering season into the warmer months, when *V. coerulea* usually takes a break from nearly continuous blooming.

Vigor also characterizes *Vanda coerulea* and its primary hybrids. *Euanthe sanderiana* or a *E. sanderiana* hybrid appear to add enough vegetative strength to permit the *V. coerulea* qualities to manifest themselves to their absolute potential. The size and profusion of flowers in *V. Rothschildiana* and other primary hybrids constantly amaze orchidists

(Plate 7-4). These primary hybrids produce more and larger flowers than either parent because of their true hybrid vigor.

The bloom display of *Vanda coerulea* is the more remarkable for being produced on such a relatively small plant. Primary *V. coerulea* hybrids, such as *V.* Rothschildiana, approach the ideal in vandas. Twenty to 30 stunningly beautiful 5-in (13-cm) blue-mauve flowers on multiple inflorescences are carried well above the foliage. They last 4–6 weeks and appear 2–4 times a year. Who could ask for anything more? An orchidist, of course!

Breeding for Improved Form and Color

Vanda hybridists sought three principal qualities: more idealized forms, fuller and flatter flowers, and a wider range of colors. Their first step was to cross *Vanda* Rothschildiana back to *Euanthe sanderiana* to produce *V.* Onomea. Whereas shape was indeed improved, the number of flowers was reduced, and the percentage of bright blues was small. Many *V.* Onomea cultivars are pink, and most of the so-called blue cultivars are, in fact, tinged with gray. When *V.* Onomea was crossed again to *E. sanderiana*, the result, *V.* Jennie Hashimoto, was almost totally dominated by *E. sanderiana*. The addition of *E. sanderiana* alone could not lead to full-formed blues.

Results were more dramatic when the strong *Euanthe sanderiana*-dominated hybrid *Vanda* Mabelmae Kamahele was crossed with *V.* Rothschildiana to produce *V.* Judy Miyamoto. Although many clones of this grex were pinks, a number emerged as dark purples. The only difference from *V.* Onomea in the parent of this hybrid was the *V. tricolor* ancestor of *V.* Mabelmae Kamahele. The impact of *Vanda tricolor*, in this and numerous other hybrids, was felt in a diffusion of color across the entire flower and in an intensification of its tones.

The influence of *Vanda tricolor* is particularly evident in the clone *V.* Judy Miyamoto 'Blue Velvet' AM/AOS. On close inspection, the overall dark color of this cultivar reveals itself to be composed of separate spots contributed by its *V. tricolor* ancestor. This clone also invariably blooms at the same times as *V. tricolor* var. *suavis*. Perhaps a fortuitous matching brought the *V. tricolor* genes to the fore in many *V.* Judy Miyamoto clones. *Vanda* Waimea, which has the *V.* Judy Miyamoto grandparent *V.* Ohuohu (*V.* Clara Shipman Fisher × *Euanthe sanderiana*) as a parent, is not noted for such intensity. It is much like an improved *V.* Onomea, with more of a subdued blue or pink of the *E. sanderiana* type. The capacity of *V. tricolor* to assert color at several generations removed was also seen in the Thai breeding of the 1970s.

Vanda Rothschildiana, when bred to other advanced *Euanthe sanderiana* hybrids, has produced good blues. *Vanda* Hilo Princess (*V.* Eisensander × *V.* Rothschildiana), registered by Masaya Miyao in 1973, exemplifies these hybrids, the finest products of Hawaiian breeders. Fortunately for everyone, the cultivar *V.* Hilo Princess 'Alice' AM/AOS has been cloned, and is widely available. This cultivar, which received its award in 1975, retains its appeal today. The numerous large mauve-blue flowers are full-formed and are carried attractively on erect stems held well above the foliage. Interestingly, *V.* Eisensander, the yellow *E. sanderiana*-type parent, has imparted more vibrancy to the color of *V.* Hilo Princess than might at first be expected. This is, however, an effect characteristic of *V. dearei* (an ancestor of *V.* Eisensander).

Modern Lines of Breeding

Dark purples and intense deep reds have characterized the best Thai hybrids of the past decade. Such hybrids as *Vanda* Hilo Princess and *V.* Judy Miyamoto have either *V. dearei* or *V. tricolor* in their ancestry, and manifest characteristics of both these species. The yellow pigments (flavanols) of both *V. dearei* and *V. tricolor* induce dark blues and purples when mixed with the blue and red pigments (anthocyanins) of *V. coerulea*. Other characteristics of *V. tricolor* and *V. dearei* are readily discernible in many modern Thai hybrids.

Vanda Gordon Dillon (*V.* Madame Rattana × *V.* Bangkok Blue) is a good starting point for understanding these complex hybrids. Different clones of *V.* Gordon Dillon range from blues to pinks because of their elaborate heredity. The blue types are well exemplified by V. Gordon Dillon 'Lea' AM/AOS (Plate 7-5), a pale bluish white flower covered with large, intensely purple-blue spots—a type of marking that became very popular in both Thailand and the United States.

The most direct source of the blue coloring is *Vanda* Bangkok Blue (*V.* Diane Ogawa × *V. coerulea*), which also has *Vanda luzonica* as a distant ancestor. But this heritage alone does not explain the pattern and the intensity of color apparent in V. Gordon Dillon.

The strong color and pattern of *Vanda* Gordon Dillon are imparted by its other, more complex parent, V. Madame Rattana, which carries the qualities that enhanced those of *V. coerulea* and *V. luzonica* in V. Bangkok Blue. One parent of V. Madame Rattana is V. Sun Tan (*V.* Beebe Sumner × *Euanthe sanderiana*). This *E. sanderiana* type is influenced by *V. tricolor*. The *V. tricolor* qualities of V. Sun Tan carry through as the vivid spots of V. Gordon Dillon 'Lea'. The other parent of V. Madame Rattana is V. Memoria Madame Pranerm (*V.* Waipuna × V. Eisenhower), a yellow flower, with reddish undertones, whose V. Waipuna parent is known to produce both yellows and blues. *Vanda dearei*'s influence from both sides of V. Memoria Madame Pranerm lent depth to the red of V. Madame Rattana and from there to V. Gordon Dillon. Despite the seeming distance in the ancestry, the qualities of *V. tricolor, V. dearei,* and *V. luzonica* are clearly evident in the flowers of V. Gordon Dillon.

As Treekul Sophonsiri pointed out in 1984 at the Eleventh World Orchid Conference, Thai growers like vandas of very deep shades of blue or red. To Thai growers, "the flower size and the number of flowers per spray are not very important," he said. Consciously or not, these preferences led Thai breeders to select parents that increased the influence of *Vanda tricolor* in their hybrids of the late 1970s and '80s. As a group, these hybrids possess many characteristics of *V. tricolor* in addition to dark color. Flower size, stem length, and number of flowers have all diminished. The darker forms of *V. tricolor* have short, sparsely flowered stems. This explains the curiosity noted by David Grove (1983). Grove pointed out that an increase in flower numbers among awarded clones brought an accompanying increase in flower size. Many awarded dark flowers were influenced by *V. tricolor*, which reduced size, flower number, stem length, and clarity of color. If the influence of *V. coerulea* is greater, both size and number of flowers increase, as Grove notes. Longer spikes and brighter colors also characterize the hybrids more influenced by *V. coerulea.*

Other features from *Vanda tricolor* appear frequently in this group of Thai hybrids. A happy effect of the increased influence of *V. tricolor* is the precociousness of these hybrids: they bloom more quickly, and on smaller plants. Many also possess the sort of heavy substance that was undreamed of in either *Euanthe sanderiana* or *V. coerulea.* Almost universally among the darker purples, the flowers display a pale peripheral edge that is present in all forms of *V. tricolor,* but not in either *E. sanderiana* or *V. coerulea.* The edges of many of these flowers are, moreover, ruffled in the manner of *V. tricolor.*

In listing those qualities that have taken second place in Thai breeding, Sophonsiri (1985) might have done well to add a third quality, shape, to the existing qualities of size and flower count. Many of these flowers (including awarded clones) have the narrow, clawed petals of *Vanda tricolor,* leaving windows between the dorsal sepal and petals. This openness is surprising in flowers whose genealogy is so dominated by *Euanthe sanderiana.* Another frequent problem is that these hybrids also have the lax flower stems of *V. tricolor.*

Vanda Kasem's Delight: An Influential Modern Parent

Vanda Kasem's Delight (*V.* Sun Tan × *V.* Thospol) is a seminal Thai hybrid that clearly shows the strong influence of *V. tricolor.* This hybrid exists in both pinks and dark purple-blues, and frequently appears in both types with nearly solid color in the lateral sepals and nearly solid petals, with an intensely spotted dorsal sepal. The color of these flowers shows their *V. tricolor* genesis in the characteristic white border. *Vanda luzonica* has had some influence also, through the *V.* Thospol parent. Neither *V. luzonica* nor *V. tricolor* are quite as spotted as they appear at first glance. *Vanda tricolor* var. *suavis* frequently has a pale cast of color over the "white" portion of the flower. *Vanda luzonica* in its darker forms, such as the cultivar 'Evelyn', opens pale pink overall, and pales further to white with pink spots. On the basis of the hybrid behavior, one might speculate on whether these spotted *Vanda* species, like such species as *Rhynchostylis gigantea*, *Aerides quinquevulnera*, and *Arachnis flos-aëris*, are capable of producing solid color forms.

Various purple clones of *Vanda* Kasem's Delight show the different qualities of *V. tricolor* carrying through the general predominance of *Euanthe sanderiana* and *V. coerulea*. The best effects of *V. tricolor* on large modern hybrids can be seen in *V.* Kasem's Delight 'The Deep' AM/AOS. The large flowers of this plant are rich purple, composed of a purple tessellation and spotting. These are overlaid with a paler cast of color on the dorsal sepal and petals, in the regions that would normally be clear pale color in *E. sanderiana*-type hybrids. In *V.* Kasem's Delight 'Triton's Treasure' AM/AOS, the color and pattern are similar, but lack textural depth. They thus present a more "matte" appearance that many find quite pleasing. *Vanda* Kasem's Delight 'Tom Boykin' AM/AOS displays the same quality. Both of the latter clones have disrupted color patterns in the petals, which appear as irregular, lighter areas in an otherwise uniform field of color. Whether this color break will be perceived as a major disqualifying fault, as it is in *Phalaenopsis* judging, remains to be seen.

Vanda Kasem's Delight appears to have been crossed more or less simultaneously with *V.* Gordon Dillon in both Florida and Thailand. The resulting hybrid, *V.* Fuchs Delight, appears in both blue-purple and pink forms, and is rapidly becoming the benchmark of modern vandas. The blue-purple forms represent a significant advance in this line of breeding. *Vanda* Fuchs Delight 'Motes Orchids' HCC/AOS is exemplary of these new purples (Plate 7-6). The round, full-formed, very substantial flowers of this cultivar are larger than the similarly dark *V.* Kasem's Delight. Their petals are broad with no windows, and, because of their excellent texture, they display the clearest purple color without dulling. Such patterning is the best of both the *V. coerulea* ancestor's tessellation and the *V. tricolor* spotting.

Having inherited some of the best traits of its *Vanda tricolor* ancestor, however, *V.* Fuchs Delight 'Motes Orchids' also inherited some of its more negative influences. The stems of this clone are short, like many others in this line of breeding, and the flowers are crowded. These faults prevented an otherwise superlative flower from attaining a higher award.

Despite their shortcomings, the new generation of purples from the
V. Gordon Dillon line are marvelously complex hybrids that have
come a very long way from *V. coerulea*.

Improved Primary Hybrids

While the modern purple-blue vandas were being developed,
interest continued in *Vanda coerulea* in Thailand. The result was the
emergence of yet more improved forms, which have been bred to the
best of the modern pinks and blues, and to spectacular effect. Many of
these primary *V. coerulea* hybrids have been awarded, reflecting a growing recognition of the superiority of this new generation of hybrids to the
so-called old V. Rothschildiana types. *Vanda* Rothschildiana, remade
with improved parents, has itself received new recognition, the clone
'Sally Roth' HCC/AOS (Plate 7-4) being superior in size and color to
previously awarded flowers. Other new hybrids of improved *V. coerulea*
crossed with advanced Thai hybrids have been taking numerous awards.
Awarded clones of V. Suwapee (*V.* Bhimayothin × *V.* coerulea), V. Motes
Blue Centurion (*V.* Motes Pioneer × *V.* coerulea), and V. Keeree's Blue
(*V.* Keeree × *V.* coerulea) are indicative of this recognition.

Perhaps the most successful of these hybrids is *Vanda* Motes Indigo.
Six clones of this grex have received AOS awards. The flowers are large,
measuring more than 6 in (15 cm) across in the largest clones. They can,
moreover, be remarkably full-formed flowers, many showing less
windowing between the petals and dorsal sepal than appears in the more
"advanced" hybrids of the previous generation, such as V. Kasem's
Delight. Colors range from clear, true blue to soft blue (as in V. Motes
Indigo 'Alice Blue' AM/AOS [Plate 7-7]), through bright lavender-blue
(*V.* Motes Indigo 'Alice' HCC/AOS), to dark indigo-blue (*V.* Motes
Indigo 'Mary Motes' HCC/AOS), to intense dark purple (*V.* Motes
Indigo 'Indigo' HCC/AOS [Plate 7-8]). These plants bloom frequently
with immense inflorescences. *Vanda* Motes Indigo 'Bart Motes'
AM/AOS carried 56 flowers on a single branched inflorescence at its
most recent flowering.

Future Possibilities

Hybrids such as *Vanda* Motes Indigo are surely among the most spectacular orchids. They are certainly an exciting improvement on a well-established standard type, but they are also more than that. They carry the potential for whole new generations of improved vandas of the more standard *Euanthe sanderiana* types. These new V. *coerulea* hybrids can help overcome the negative V. *tricolor* traits of small size, short, weak stems, and muddy color, which were bred into vandas in the search for even darker colors. *Vanda* Bangkok Blue, a primary V. *coerulea* hybrid, contributed much of the positive qualities in V. Gordon Dillon, which has exerted such a pervasive influence in modern breeding. When bred to modern hybrids such as *Vanda* Fuchs Delight, V. Motes Indigo and the other new hybrids can be expected to produce a new generation of blue-purple *Vanda* hybrids that preserve the best of the dark purples while also overcoming many of their faults.

One can expect dark, full-formed flowers on long stems with vivid, clear colors (Plate 7-9). Many of these precocious hybrids will carry many more and larger flowers, and will flower more often. Unlike crosses between two complex hybrids, these new, second-generation *Vanda coerulea* hybrids will possess greater consistency, yielding a high percentage of very desirable plants and few, if any, of the disastrous specimens that all too often result from breeding a complex hybrid to a complex hybrid. One also can expect that these new hybrids will be sibling-crossed, and that the new secondary hybrids will once more be bred to yet further improved V. *coerulea* clones and to the best of the new siblings. By borrowing some of the best qualities of V. *tricolor* and V. *luzonica*, blue hybrids will continue to grow larger, fuller, darker, and more floriferous (Plate 7-10).

Eight

New Directions in *Vanda* Breeding

Nearly all the strap-leaved *Vanda* hybrids currently grown have only five species in their background: *Euanthe sanderiana*, *V. coerulea*, *V. tricolor*, *V. luzonica*, and *V. dearei*. The success of selective breeding from these species can thus be seen in our modern hybrids, whose color and pattern were inherited from just four true *Vanda* species. A mere 10% of the genetic potential of the 40 *Vanda* species has therefore been tapped.

Perhaps this is the result of our having thought of *Vanda* species simply as "good" or "bad." *Phalaenopsis* was traditionally regarded in a very similar way, and indeed *Vanda* breeding is currently at the stage reached by *Phalaenopsis* breeding some 25 years ago. Vandas were "discovered" as serious horticultural plants even later than *Phalaenopsis*, and, like *Phalaenopsis* in the 1960s, their culture is just beginning to be understood by the majority of northern growers. Interest in vandas is now increasing rapidly. Breeders are beginning to realize that these plants will bloom 2, 3, or even more times per year, and that the flowers will last for 4–6 weeks (far longer per year than even *Phalaenopsis*). This growing awareness has sparked a demand for ever greater variety in these already varied flowers. The possibilities are immense.

Improving Modern Vandas

Vanda hybridists, just like hybridists of *Phalaenopsis* in the 1960s and '70s, must now begin to introduce characteristics of additional species to the already nearly perfected standard lines of breeding. There certainly is potential to exploit single qualities in otherwise uninspiring *Vanda* species. Hybridists would do well to look at the remarkable work in yellow and spotted *Phalaenopsis* begun by Lewis and Varina Vaughn, and at the creation of striped *Phalaenopsis* and whites with red lips (both of which are now standards).

Many of the early hybrids made with *Vanda* species were less than satisfactory because the *Euanthe sanderiana* types to which they were matched were far from showing the degree of perfection commonplace today. The fuller-formed and larger flowers of modern standard vandas, when bred to *Vanda* species, produce hybrids markedly superior to those of the 1950s and '60s.

Hybrids of *Euanthe sanderiana* in cultivation are usually referred to as *strap-leaf vandas*. In fact, as Plate 8-1 shows, *E. sanderiana* has a deeply V-shaped leaf. This quality, perhaps an adaptation to its lowland equatorial habitat in the Philippines (where the plants are subjected to strong sunlight directly overhead), makes *E. sanderiana* and its hybrids very poorly adapted to temperate climates. For much of the year, light in such climates is at a low angle of incidence, and temperatures are much lower. Outside of the tropics, leaves of this shape are extremely inefficient for most of the year. True vandas, on the other hand, have *strap leaves*, as shown in Plate 8-1. This flat, broad leaf surface (which is carried to its fullest extent in *Phalaenopsis*) is very effective in gathering light, and hence in stimulating growth. The root systems of true vandas, such as *Vanda* Motes Raspberry Cream (Plate 8-2), are vigorous. The plants throw aerial roots from relatively young tissue, allowing them to react quickly to changed conditions or setbacks. In contrast, *E. sanderiana* and its hybrids root from much older tissue near the base of the plant, and hence are slower to respond and renew if damaged.

These differences were not lost on the European hybridists of the early 20th century. While *Euanthe sanderiana* does figure in the early German and French hybrids, *Vanda coerulea*, *V. tricolor*, and *V. tricolor* var. *suavis* (then considered a separate species) were held in equally high esteem. *Vanda coerulea* has continued to enjoy popularity, and increasingly so with the availability of the improved Thai strains. *Vanda tricolor*, however, has been little used in later decades. Perhaps part of the reason for its partial eclipse lies in the negative qualities of the dull yellow-brown variety *planilabris*, which early Hawaiian growers dubbed *V. tricolor* "plenty rubbish." The variety *suavis*, on the other hand, has exceptional color—rich purple-red spots overlaying a white ground, with a vivid purple lip.

Potential of *Vanda tricolor* var. *suavis*

Fortunately, *Vanda tricolor* var. *suavis* passes its color pattern on to its progeny in a rich variety of hues. *Vanda tricolor* var. *suavis* possesses significant potential to produce flowers with strong color juxtaposed on a pale background. Among the first hybrids attempted was a remake of the early hybrid *V.* Burgeffii, using a modern *Euanthe sanderiana*. The results were good: the hybrid possessed vigorous, free-flowering plants with open-formed flowers. Although unlikely to win an AOS judge's approval, the flowers were bright enough and profuse enough to impress most people.

Similar results were obtained with the remake of *V.* Herziana: exceptionally vigorous plants producing multitudes of fragrant, bright blue flowers with darker purple spots. The flowers are carried on long stems, which appear in nearly constant succession, scarcely waiting for the last flower of the previous spike to fade before opening afresh. These are different in every way from the typical *Vandanthe*. They cannot be judged by typical standards—but why would one feel the need to do so? The original remake of *V.* Herziana used an improved, so-called jungle-type *V. coerulea*. But the latest remake uses a state-of-the-art, "Thai-improved" type that should result in fuller, larger flowers close to conformity with contemporary judging standards.

When crossed to the modern blue hybrid *Vanda* Princess Blue (*V.* Jennie Hashimoto × *V. coerulea*), *V. tricolor* var. *suavis* predictably produced spotted progeny that were larger and fuller than V. Herziana, and still dependably fragrant. This hybrid, V. Starre Gypsy, came in shades of pale purple to blue to pink, due to the mixed ancestry of the *Vandanthe* parent, and is being followed by hybrids between V. *tricolor* var. *suavis* and very modern V. *coerulea* hybrids. Crossing to the finest V. Motes Indigo, V. Wirat, and other exceptional hybrids has yielded offspring that are larger, fuller, and more deeply colored. Some of these crosses have begun to flower at about 4 years from seed, a rapid maturity due to breeding with true vandas, and the best are fulfilling expectations. One of these hybrids, V. Mood Indigo (V. Motes Indigo × V. *tricolor* var. *suavis*), has received an HCC. The fragrant, full-formed flowers resembled a larger, better shaped V. *tricolor* var. *suavis*. This innovation proved irresistible to neophyte and connoisseur alike. Two others of the same grex, in a blue-spotted pattern, have also received AOS recognition.

The greatest success so far achieved in breeding *Vanda tricolor* var. *suavis* was the product of crossing it with V. *cristata*. This effectively remade V. Paki, first registered by Herbert Shipman in 1946. Whether Shipman used the variety *suavis*, then considered a separate species, or, as the registration shows, V. *tricolor* (i.e., the brown form), is unknown. The modern remake using V. *tricolor* var. *suavis* has produced impressive results. The pale green flowers, vividly spotted with red, and a startling contrast with the large red lip, are arresting. Seven of these have received AOS award recognition. *Vanda* Paki (Plate 8-3) is a superlative pot plant: relatively small, vigorous growth, flowering 3–4 times per year. The fragrant flowers gradually fade from green to white during their 2 months in bloom.

Secondary hybrids of *Vanda* Paki crossed to standard whites (i.e., *Euanthe sanderiana* var. *alba* types) and yellows should produce larger, fuller-formed flowers that preserve the distinctive color patterns of V. Paki. The first of these hybrids, V. Motes Goldflake, flowered in 39 months from seed; one of the grex received an HCC in 1993.

A similar hybrid from *Vanda tricolor* var. *suavis* was made with *Vanda* (*Trudelia*) *pumila*. Registered as V. Agatha Motes, these produced milk-white flowers clearly spotted with red and contrasted with a large, dark red lip (Plate 8-4). The large lips of V. *cristata* (Plate 8-5) and V. *pumila* are the most prominent aesthetic features of both. The lip is not only the brightest but also the largest floral part. This feature is carried on into the progeny of both species. Although untested and untried in our warm South Florida greenhouses, this hybrid should possess great cold tolerance, and should grow and flower at much lower temperatures than *Euanthe sanderiana*.

When crossed with *Ascocenda* Yip Sum Wah, *Vanda tricolor* var. *suavis* yielded very happy results. *Ascocenda* Ann Reaben Prospero produces medium-sized flowers whose base color ranges from pale pink to pale yellow to very bright yellow. In all color forms, the base color is richly overlaid with bright red polka dots (Plate 8-6). As with many other *V. tricolor* var. *suavis* hybrids, the flowers are somewhat larger than initially expected, some approaching in size those of *V. tricolor* var. *suavis* itself. The clone *Ascocenda* Ann Reaben Prospero 'Most Articulate Lady' HCC/AOS possessed clear color, relatively full form, and a long, erect spike that displayed the striking flowers to best advantage. A second clone of even fuller shape has been recognized.

When bred to ascocendas, *Vanda tricolor* var. *suavis*, like other *Vanda* species, not infrequently produces progeny that are fuller in form than those which result when *Vanda* species are bred to *Euanthe sanderiana* and its hybrids. (See, for example, the clone of *Ascocenda* Ann Reaben Prospero, illustrated in Plate 8-6.) The reason for this lies, perhaps, in the different shape of the *Ascocentrum* petal. Unlike the clawed petal of the *Vanda* species, the *Ascocentrum* petal is quite broad at the base, creating full-formed, "windowless" flowers in the best *Ascocentrum* clones.

Overall, *Vanda tricolor* var. *suavis* is an outstanding parent. It produces vigorous, free-flowering, precocious progeny that are both brightly colored and clearly marked. *Vanda tricolor* var. *suavis* also favorably influences the blooming season of its offspring. Since it responds to both shortening and lengthening daylight intervals, it confers strong tendencies to bloom in the desirable April–May and November–December periods. Spring-blooming *Vanda* species, when crossed to the fall-blooming *Euanthe sanderiana* and its hybrids, produce progeny similar to the free-flowering hybrids of *Ascocentrum*. Indeed, the "*Ascocenda*-like" indeterminate blooming habits of primary hybrids that were descended from *V. tricolor* var. *suavis* and other true *Vanda* species were a major factor in their early acceptance as horticultural subjects. *Vanda tricolor* var. *suavis* might be thought of as the vandaceous breeding equivalent of *Cattleya aurantiaca*, in that *V. tricolor* var. *suavis* produces hybrids that are slightly smaller and shaped a little differently from standard types, but with vivid color and with plants of robust growth.

Much more remains to be done with *Vanda tricolor* var. *suavis*. It has been bred to many other ascocendas in the hope of producing new successes after the pattern of *Ascocenda* Ann Reaben Prospero. Many advanced *Vanda* hybrids in purples, pinks, and reds show a strong influence from *V. tricolor* var. *suavis*. *Vanda* Gordon Dillon 'Lea' is an excellent example of this sort of flower. *Vanda tricolor* var. *suavis* has been bred to *V.* Gordon Dillon 'Lea' and other hybrids of this clear purple- or red-spotted color pattern with the expectation of accentuating the color and producing fragrant, free-flowering, vigorous plants. This expectation is probably well founded. The seedlings of *V.* First and Last (*V.* Fuchs Delight 'Motes Orchids' × *V. tricolor* var. *suavis*) have flowered with the bold dappling of the *V. tricolor* parent, despite the overall dark purple of *V.* Fuchs Delight. One of these seedlings was chosen Best Vanda at the 1996 Fort Lauderdale show, and a second received an AM/AOS. The best of these could be bred back to standard types in order to further enhance this desirable pattern in yet fuller flowers.

Potential of *Vanda luzonica*

Vanda luzonica, once considered a variety of *V. tricolor*, is another species with great breeding potential. One very successful early European hybrid is *V.* Boschii (*V. luzonica* × *V. tricolor* var. *suavis*), which was registered just 9 years after *V. luzonica* was published as a species. Many of the plants in cultivation labeled *V. luzonica* (including three clones awarded by the AOS) are in fact *V.* Boschii. These plants can easily be distinguished from one another, since *V. luzonica* is scentless, while *V. tricolor* transmits its strong fragrance to its progeny (including *V.* Boschii). One need only look through old Hawaiian collections for species vandas and early primary hybrids to see that most of the survivors from the early hybrids are in fact *V.* Boschii.

This testament to the vigor of the true *Vanda* hybrids is even more evident in light of the virtual nonexistence of second- or third-generation

Euanthe sanderiana hybrids. One clone of V. Boschii, 'Nishida Orchids' HCC/AOS, has received AOS recognition. This clone appears indistinguishable from V. *luzonica* 'Evelyn' AM/AOS. By whatever name, the enduring appeal of V. Boschii's brightly marked crimson and white flowers is apparent.

Vanda luzonica is the chief source of the bright pink color in modern *Vanda* hybrids. Crossed to *Euanthe sanderiana*, it produced V. Manila, a bright pink hybrid, which in turn produced V. Bill Sutton, a cornerstone of pink breeding. Happily, V. *luzonica*'s color is dominant over nearly all other *Vanda* color. It also contributes vigor and long, many-flowered stems to its progeny.

An interesting example of *Vanda luzonica*'s breeding characteristics is the new primary hybrid V. Motes Raspberry Cream (V. *luzonica* × V. *bensonii*). The long stem of V. *bensonii* is complemented by the same quality in V. *luzonica*, but the most interesting result of this hybrid is the dominance of V. *luzonica*'s color over the chestnut-brown of V. *bensonii*, which one would assume to be more dominant. Plants of the grex have begun blooming as early as 4 years old, and produced spikes almost without pause. These are being bred to large-flowered, standard pink vandas in the hope of producing medium-sized pinks of heavy substance on long stems.

Similarly, *Vanda luzonica* itself is being bred to modern standard pinks. Bred to such marvelously full-formed flowers as V. Fuchs Delight 'Motes Jubilation' AM/AOS, a new generation of full-formed pinks of great vigor is expected. Because of the fullness of modern hybrids, these crosses may in just one generation accomplish as much, in terms of shape, as earlier hybridists accomplished in two to three generations.

A new variety of *Vanda luzonica* has been discovered. The variety *immaculata* (Plate 8-7) has pure white sepals and petals (which fade to cream after the flowers have been open a few days) with a brilliant cerise lip. Using this variety, the potential is there to create white vandas with colored lips. Hybrids between V. *luzonica* var. *immaculata*, *Euanthe sanderiana* var. *alba*, and white hybrids such as V. Rasri Gold are currently in progress, but the breeding characteristics of this new variety are as yet largely unknown. The single hybrid to bloom thus far, V. *luzonica* var. *immaculata* × V. *tessellata* var. *alba*, was cream-yellow with a startling blue lip.

Golden Prospects from *Vanda denisoniana*

Vanda denisoniana has enormous potential as a parent of both concolor and spotted yellows, as well as of pastels in a variety of hues. This pale, night-fragrant flower behaves, in hybrids, much like the night-pollinated New World genera *Rhyncolaelia*, *Brassavola*, and *Diacrium* (i.e., it mutes the color of colored flowers bred to it). This quality of *V. denisoniana* emerged clearly in the modern remake of *Ascocenda* Tavivat (*V. denisoniana* × *Ascda.* Meda Arnold). The result might be thought of as a Mendelian segregation of the complex ancestry of the *Ascocenda* parent. The progeny ranged in color from clear yellow to orange to red to red-bronze, to pink to pale blue to purple. Concolor, spotted, and striped forms all emerged, perhaps because *V. denisoniana* itself is so variable. Most clones show some introgression from the natural hybrid swarm that has caused so many taxonomic difficulties to botanists studying the Thai and Burmese species related to *V. denisoniana*.

This complexity of results is one of the problems related to breeding with *Vanda denisoniana*. On the other hand, this is also one of the more exciting aspects of breeding with this species. The variability in *V. denisoniana* hybrids is itself a delight, but it also offers a bewildering array of possibilities for future breeding. For example, *V.* Motes Honeybun (*V.* Kultana Gold × *V. denisoniana*) produced mostly red to brown spotted flowers like those of the awarded clone 'Golden Dawn' HCC/AOS—lovely in themselves and a building block for substantial, spotted yellows. A few individuals, however, were a clear, bright yellow of a resplendence not seen in yellow breeding from *V. dearei* lines. Assuming these to be genetically uniform for this clear bright color, they were bred to bright yellows from *V. dearei* lines, such as *V.* Phetchaburi Gold and *V.* Rasri Gold. The expectation is that these will be large flowers of excellent substance and clear color that will set a new standard for yellows. The first to bloom have fulfilled much of this expectation, although none has yet proved as full-formed as desired.

Vanda Motes Honeybun crossed with *V. tricolor* var. *suavis* produced the vividly spotted yellow *V.* Meg Laughlin, itself a potentially valuable parent of striking yellows. One of this grex received an AM in 1995 and a second an HCC in 1996. *Vanda denisoniana* has also been crossed to

V. cristata, from which have emerged both spotted and concolor yellows with red lips. *Vanda denisoniana* has an excellent record as a parent of ascocendas, but its potential in breeding vandas is still largely untapped.

Potential of *Vanda stangeana*

Vanda stangeana (Plate 8-8) is a tessellated yellow species from India that produces its 2-in (5-cm) flowers on relatively tiny plants. Its neglect by early hybridists was unfortunate. The potential to breed tessellated yellows is its first attraction, but the first hybrids to flower have revealed further desirable qualities. Perhaps chief among these is the ability to flower early, on small plants, and then to continue flowering, virtually unabated. The tessellated pattern that appears chestnut-brown in the species emerges in its hybrids as a much brighter red. The large, distinctively shaped (and in some clones, colored) lip also carries through to its progeny.

Although *Vanda stangeana* has been used in the past for several intergeneric hybrids, the first straight *Vanda* hybrid is the new primary *V.* Motes Ginger Pied (*V. stangeana* × *V. tricolor* var. *suavis*) (Plate 8-9). The medium-sized flowers show the tessellated pattern of *V. stangeana* in a not altogether unpleasant reddish brown shade. The most endearing features of this new primary hybrid are its free-flowering habit and strong fragrance.

Vanda stangeana crossed to *Ascocenda* Bonanza produced *Ascda*. Rose Sutton (Plate 8-10), which flowered on small plants at 4 years from seed. The best clones will produce 6–8 flower spikes per year on plants of quite small size. Most range in color from pale pink to pale yellow, but some are deep brick-red. All are heavily overlaid with bright reddish tessellation and spots. The distinctive pink color and bifurcated shape of the *V. stangeana* lip also carries through. The success of this hybrid has led to the crossing of *V. stangeana* with other ascocendas, in the hope of producing free-flowering, diminutive plants with interesting new color patterns.

Vanda stangeana has been crossed to large-flowered yellows that show some tendency toward tessellated patterns. The progeny of *V.* Motes Butterscotch with *V. stangeana* did not produce the desired pattern, but when V. *stangeana* was crossed to a more distinctly tessellated parent, V. Thai Checkers (Plate 8-11), the seedlings were sharply tessellated yellows of heavy substance, which bloomed early on compact plants. The hope is that these hybrids, like *Ascocenda* hybrids from V. *stangeana*, will continue to be free-flowering.

The interesting pink to red markings of some clones of *Ascocenda* Rose Sutton has opened up new avenues in pink breeding, through the crossing of *Vanda stangeana* to large pink vandas that show the tessellated pattern of their V. *coerulea* ancestry. The hope is to produce tessellated pink- to red-toned flowers of medium size on small, vigorous plants. The full potential of V. *stangeana* as a parent has yet to be explored or evaluated.

Vanda merrillii's Potential for Reds

Vanda merrillii is an exceptionally attractive, sweetly fragrant species that bears long stems of 2-in (5-cm) yellow flowers heavily overlaid with dark red. In some clones, this dark red covers the entire flower. These are sometimes referred to as var. Rotor. The effect of this strong color is intensified by a waxy, highly lacquered texture (Plate 8-12). This distinctive color and texture were noted by the early Hawaiian hybridists, who produced several hybrids from V. *merrillii*. The most enduringly successful is V. Trimerrill, a free-flowering, yellow and red-brown flower very frequently labeled V. *merrillii* in modern collections. Some secondary *Vanda* hybrids were produced, but perhaps the most successful line of early breeding from V. *merrillii* was with ascocendas.

Ascocenda Red Gem (*Vanda merrillii* × *Ascocentrum curvifolium*) is a free-flowering, concolor red bloom on a long stem. Selfings made in both Florida and Thailand produced a wide range of color while preserving the lacquered texture of V. *merrillii*. A modern hybrid of the same type, *Ascda*. Ruby Tuesday (*Ascda*. Truman Motes × V. *merrillii*), received an AM/AOS in 1996. *Vanda* Somthawil (V. *denisoniana* × V. *merrillii*) was first registered in 1975 by the Thai breeder Chuanyen. In the remake, many of the best qualities of both species emerged. Vigorous and free-flowering plants, they produce long spikes of yellow flowers overlaid with brown to red. By 1993, four had received AOS recognition. In the awarded clone 'Bill Burke' AM/AOS (Plate 8-13), the somewhat lax lateral spike carried 14 flowers of a lacquered chestnut-red color.

Some growers have bred with *Vanda merrillii* only sporadically, in part due to *V. merrillii*'s deceptively short-lived flowers. Although they appear heavy and waxy, the flowers usually last only 2 weeks. Breeders accustomed to allowing flowers to mature for several days before attempting to pollinate them have frequently allowed the flowers of *V. merrillii* to fade before hybridization was attempted. One of the most successful hybrids to date is *Ascocenda* Motes Bloodstone (*Ascda.* Bonanza × *V. merrillii*). These have been brilliantly colored, with an ivory-yellow base color heavily mottled with dark blood-red (Plate 8-14). Another mark in its favor is its tendency to flower young and often. One clone of this grex has been awarded in recent years.

A similar hybrid, *Vanda merrillii* × *Ascocenda* Bigness, flowered with a quite similar pattern in a slightly larger flower. Two of these received AOS award recognition in 1996. Both this hybrid and *Ascda.* Motes Bloodstone have such a strong resemblance to *V. merrillii* that they might easily be mistaken for the species.

By crossing these not only to other ascocendas, but also back to *Vanda merrillii* itself, one can expect to produce better shaped, highly textured red flowers. Such crossing back should produce fragrant, free-flowering plants. Unlike *V. merrillii* itself, the flowers will be long-lasting and will bloom several times a year.

Because of the wonderful color of *Vanda merrillii*, and its marvelous texture (which carries through several generations of hybrids), some growers are vigorously pursuing hybrids with standard pink and blue vandas. The hope is that second- and third-generation hybrids will carry *V. merrillii*'s texture and color into full-formed, large flowers.

Potential of *Vanda tessellata*

Vanda tessellata has been used periodically in *Vanda* bloodlines, but many of its virtues have yet to be fully exploited in *Vanda* breeding.

Vanda tessellata is a relatively small plant of great vegetative vigor. Its natural range is extensive, and it occurs in many color forms. Most forms are tessellated gray or brown with a bright blue or pink lip.

Forms of *Vanda tessellata* in cultivation in Thailand, said to have originated in Sri Lanka, are larger and concolor gray, purple, and red-brown. An *alba* form (Plate 8-15) also exists. These forms may have some hybrid blood in them (perhaps from *V. dearei*), but the consistency, in both color and form, displayed by large groups of seedlings suggests that these are at least a subspecies. They are superior to the typical species in both size and color, although they flower less frequently. Bred in Thailand to *V. coerulea*, these *V. tessellatas* produced a new strain of *V.* Violeta with bright, cobalt-blue flowers on long stems and of very heavy substance, which has garnered several AOS awards.

Vanda tessellata f. *alba* bred to *Vanda* Thananchai produced *V.* Thanantess, which in most forms is gray-green with a violet lip. One clone release (as a meristem) is nearly pure white with a pale blue lip (Plate 8-16). This plant holds some potential for breeding a white with blue- or violet-colored lip in a standard *Vanda* flower. Motes Orchids has bred these to *Euanthe sanderiana* var. *alba* and to *alba*-hybrid types, such as *V.* Rasri Gold. Bred to other white types with colored lip, such as *V. pumila* and *V. cristata*, bridge hybrids could be created to use in creating large-flowered whites with colored lips. One such primary hybrid, *V. tessellata* var. *alba* × *V. luzonica* var. *immaculata*, has flowered with nearly white, blue-lipped blooms.

Strongly two-toned flowers with a vividly contrasting lip are characteristic, too, of the hybrids of the typical color form of *Vanda tessellata*. The most successful of these is the deliciously fragrant *V.* Mimi Palmer (*V.* Tan Chay Yan × *V. tessellata*). Clones of this grex have received award recognition both in Thailand and from the AOS—and for good reason. The steely blue-gray mottled petals and sepals are a perfect background for the startling violet-blue lip (Plate 8-17).

These clones have the appearance of a very superior form of the Thai-cultivated *Vanda tessellata*, hinting that these forms might have had some influence from this hybrid. Breeding the Thai variety to *V. tricolor* var. *suavis* has produced fragrant, pale bluish and pinkish, heavily spotted flowers of medium size, with bright blue or pink lips. One of these,

V. Motes Toledo Blue 'Gro-more', received an HCC in 1994 and two others were awarded in 1996. Bred to *V.* Princess Blue, *V.* Mimi Palmer produces pale blue-gray flowers with vivid lips. *Vanda* Blue Grig (*V.* Rothschildiana × *V. tessellata*) produced dark blues that have proved popular. Backcrossed to *V. tessellata*, the remake of *V.* Arjuna received three AOS awards in 1996 for its glossy flowers with brilliant violet lips. Through hybrids such as *V.* Mimi Palmer and *V.* Thanantess, *V. tessellata* has the potential to contribute much to the color patterns of *Vanda*.

Vanda bensonii's Potential for Long Stems

Vanda bensonii (Plate 8-18), a species closely related to *V. tessellata*, also possesses a vivid violet to pink lip, contrasted with sepals and petals of a rich chestnut-brown. Its exceptionally long inflorescence, to 30 in (75 cm), carries its flowers well above the foliage and widely spaced. The potential of *V. bensonii* to produce long-stemmed yellows (overcoming the *V. dearei* influence for short stems) led to breeders' crossing *V. bensonii* to *V.* Queen Kaumana (a standard *Euanthe sanderiana*-type yellow). The result, *V.* Motes Nutmeg, was chestnut-brown, medium-sized flowers held well above the foliage. While it is not vivid in color, this hybrid does possess a dignified beauty that is derived from its waxy texture and even, uniform coloring. It demonstrates how *V. bensonii* can be quite dominant, for both color and stem length, when bred to yellows. 'Redland Spice' (Plate 8-19), a clone of the grex, received an HCC in 1993.

When bred to pinks, as with *Vanda* Motes Raspberry Cream, *V. bensonii* is less dominant. When *V. bensonii* is bred to blues, the effect is to deepen the color to a dark purple. *Ascocenda* Nopawan (*Ascda.* Ooi Boon Huat × *V. bensonii*) is an excellent example. The deep purple flowers are carried on long stems and are widely spaced, thus overcoming one of the chief faults in most ascocendas. *Ascocenda* Nopawan was bred in Thailand to *V. coerulea* to produce long-stemmed blues suitable for use as cut flowers. This line of breeding is also valuable for potted plants, as most ascocendas are fairly long-stemmed but tend to crowd their flowers.

Much of the breeding potential of *Vanda bensonii* will be realized in second- and third-generation hybrids. Motes Orchids has bred *V.* Motes

Nutmeg to blues such as *V.* Motes Indigo and *V.* Wirat to produce long-stemmed, heavily substantial dark blues. Similarly, *Ascocenda* Nopawan and its hybrids are being bred to blue-toned ascocendas to produce long-stemmed, well-spaced flowers of intense color.

Potential of *Vanda cristata*

Vanda cristata (considered by some botanists to belong to the newly determined genus *Trudelia*) has many virtues. These plants are compact, and can produce up to 8 inflorescences at a time. Both qualities could make a desirable impact on *Vanda* bloodlines. Its color (clear greenish yellow sepals, and petals contrasting with a crimson lip) is impressive, and its potential to produce similar color patterns in larger-flowered hybrids is exciting. The striking lip of the species is the brightest, and by far the largest, floral segment.

Vanda cristata transmits its large lip to its progeny. When *V. cristata* was crossed with the equally large-lipped *V. insignis*, the result was *V.* Kekaseh (Plate 8-20). *Kekaseh* means *sweetheart* in Malay, and the hybrid is aptly named. It continually produces 2-in (5-cm) yellow flowers, heavily mottled with golden brown, and with a large, broad, vivid crimson lip. The small stature and free-flowering nature of this fragrant hybrid make it a wonderful pot plant that would brighten any collection.

A similarly successful primary hybrid is *Vanda* Mellow Days (*V. cristata* × *V. merrillii*). The yellow-spotted flowers possess the vivid lip of *V. cristata* and the lustrous texture of *V. merrillii*. Like *V.* Kekaseh, these splendid plants are seldom without their charmingly fragrant flowers. The clone 'John Ward' (Plate 8-21) won the trophy as best *Vanda* in show at the Tropical Orchid Society show in West Palm Beach, Florida, illustrating both the appeal and the growing acceptance of the best of the new *Vanda* bloodlines.

In the 1950s, *Vanda cristata* was crossed to *Euanthe sanderiana* to produce *V.* Joan Yuhas. This hybrid was subsequently remade using *E. sanderiana* f. *alba*. These have bloomed at little more than 3 years from seed and produced relatively large green flowers with red lips. The color effect is somewhat muted by some tessellation from the *E. sanderiana* parent. The plants continue to bloom many times a year, and have potential as building blocks toward a white-with-red-lip *Vanda*. One clone received an AM in 1996.

Vanda Paki, the successful hybrid of *V. cristata* and *V. tricolor* discussed earlier in this chapter, was crossed to V. Rasri Gold—a large *alba* type—to produce V. Motes Gold Flake, another precocious, free-flowering miniature hybrid. All of these have white sepals and petals with a vivid red lip that is almost as intense as that of their *V. cristata* grand-parent. The first clone to receive AOS recognition was 'Mary Motes', which was awarded an HCC. *Vanda* Motes Gold Flake 'Mary Motes' is green, and lightly spotted with crimson in the manner of *V. tricolor* var. *suavis*. The similar hybrid *V*. David Junka (*V*. Kultana Gold × *V. cristata*) has been recognized with an Award of Distinction and two AMs.

Secondary hybrids from *Vanda* Kekaseh and *V*. Mellow Days could produce a similar line of spotted and mottled yellows with prominent red lips. The most successful to date is *V*. Singapore Sweetheart (*V*. Kekaseh × *V*. Singapore Sunshine) 'Mary Motes' AM/AOS (Plate 8-22), which illustrates the charm of vividly colored vandas used as compact pot plants.

Potential of *Vanda pumila*

Closely related to *Vanda cristata*, the species *V. pumila* also has great potential in breeding white vandas with colored lips. The even smaller size of the plant is an advantage that *V. pumila* enjoys over *V. cristata* in the line of breeding, although *V. cristata* does carry more flowers per stem than *V. pumila* and can transmit this quality to its progeny. Based on the comparison between *V*. Paki and *V*. Agatha Motes (*V. tricolor* × *V. pumila*), one might surmise that *V. pumila* would breed larger, whiter flowers on shorter, fewer-flowered stems. Bred to *V. lamellata* var. *reme-diosa*, it produced *V*. Christel Morgenroth, which first flowered at an incredible 29 months from seed. The 3-in (6-cm) tall plants continue to produce spikes of 6–8 fragrant, 1.5-in (3.5-cm) flowers, several times per year.

Other Vandas with Potential

The finer, paler forms of *Vanda lamellata* var. *remediosa* (Plate 8-23) might have an impact on standard white or light-colored breeding. Unlike V. *pumila*, V. *lamellata* var. *remediosa* carries a multitude (up to 30) of flowers on long stems. But like V. *cristata* and V. *pumila*, V. *lamellata* produces as many as 8 flower spikes simultaneously.

This floral profusion could be an addition to the bloodlines of several color forms of vandas. The distinctive markings of both *Vanda lamellata* var. *remediosa* and the brilliantly colored variety *boxalli* (Plate 8-24) could prove alluring in larger hybrids, particularly since the advent of the Award of Quality strain that has received so many awards. The success of ascocendas such as the frequently awarded *Ascocenda* Khun Nok augurs well for V. *lamellata* as a parent, even though this species appears to breed more readily with ascocendas than with vandas. Many new hybrids are coming to maturity, and the first show great promise. One, *Ascda.* Ginger Hot, the result of crossing V. *lamellata* var. *boxalli* with a brilliant golden *Ascda.* Motes Goldenrod, received an HCC/AOS in May 1995. *Ascocenda* Motes Burning Sands (V. *lamellata* var. *boxalli* × *Ascda.* Motes Goldpiece) also received award recognition for its bright, clearly marked flowers. The hybrid of V. *lamellata* var. *boxalli* with V. Rasri Gold produced larger, boldly marked flowers, and one clone garnered an AM.

Other *Vanda* species also show the potential to contribute one or more distinctive qualities. *Vanda lindenii* could pass on its distinctive color pattern and strong fragrance, V. *roeblingiana* its ornate lip and cold tolerance, and V. *insignis* the large, brilliant lip already passed on to such strap-leaved hybrids as V. Joan Warne (Plate 8-25). The breeding qualities of many species have not been even remotely exploited to the full, and some are so rare in cultivation that their contributions may not be felt for decades to come. The success of the breeding already done from the true *Vanda* species should encourage hybridists to pursue the wide range of possibilities inherent in this most misunderstood and ignored group of plants.

Looking Ahead

Many vigorous, adaptable hybrids bred from true *Vanda* species have been successfully crossed to ascocendas and vandanthes from standard bloodlines. This bodes well for the future of *Vanda* hybrids in greenhouse cultivation. Careful selection of the most productive, colorful, and disease-resistant plants should make a whole new range of flowers accessible to both hobbyists and florists. Many of these will, of course, be clones that embody the best achievements of modern hybridization. It is somewhat ironic that modern technology will be responsible for bringing to the homes of the 21st century some of the darlings of Victorian orchidists.

In order to achieve acceptance for some of the truly new directions in *Vanda* breeding, certain aesthetic prejudices need to be challenged. The first of these is that which proclaims only flowers of the *Euanthe sanderiana* type to be truly beautiful. This is the same type of sensibility that gave us extra-large lavender cattleyas and "tea cup" paphiopedilums. For some, these types will remain the only beautiful cattleyas and paphiopedilums. Others, of more catholic sensibilities, find it easier to see beauty in many species of these genera and in the primary hybrids manifesting the positive qualities of the species.

The second prejudice grew out of a simple misperception. Contrary to popular opinion, many early *Vanda* hybrids—such as *V.* Gilbert Triboulet, *V.* Flammerolle, and *V.* Violeta—did not lose *inherent* beauty or appeal but were merely superseded by changing tastes. This had also been the case with the original *Sophrocattleya* Batemanniana, *Paphiopedilum* Iona, and *Phalaenopsis* Cassandra.

Tempus fugit. Breeders who prize novelty not for its own sake but for the aesthetic potential beyond the cliché may find comfort in the following: it is the frequently expressed opinion of many orchid show observers that *Vanda* Mary's Dimity 'Mary's Dimity' and some of its siblings are not merely beautiful, but the "most beautiful" vandas they have ever seen. Beauty is, indeed, in the eye of the beholder!

The early *Vanda* hybridists surely could not have dreamed of the degree of perfection that would be achieved by line breeding from *Euanthe sanderiana*, *V. coerulea*, *V. luzonica*, *V. tricolor*, and *V. dearei*.

Their objectives were more limited: namely, to create improvements in existing types and to make good hybrids. The advent of cloning was beyond their horizons.

One is almost tempted to liken the orchidists of the past to the great Italian poet, lost in a dark forest of error. The path is now clear, and yet the goals of modern *Vanda* hybridists are somewhat different. Mericloning is now a straightforward and commonplace procedure, and the hybridist's goal is to produce crosses that will yield individuals of exceptional quality. Through cloning, these individuals can become part of the permanent heritage of orchidists everywhere.

Complex and rapid advances can be made in the hybridization of vandas. Today's standard types will continue to be bred, but the future holds so much more in terms of new colors, new patterns, miniaturization, and fragrances. The playwright George Bernard Shaw once said of marriage that it provided "the maximum of temptation with the maximum of opportunity." Hybridists might be tempted to say the same of vandas, whose multiple inflorescences will be available to them several times each year. And what orchidist was ever able to resist the temptation of adding another hue to the rainbow?

Nine

Vanda Culture

Vandas achieved prominence later than any of the major horticultural genera of orchids. But the last 40 years have brought an increasing sophistication in their culture. Growers in both the tropics and more temperate areas have mastered the requirements of these plants, and many impressive specimens have been displayed and awarded.

The skills necessary to grow vandas to a high degree of perfection are unfortunately still the property of a relatively small group of growers. Luckily, vandas are very tolerant plants and easily grown in a fairly rough-hewn way, repaying even moderate attention with an elaborate show of flowers. This inherent vigor makes vandas rewarding even for the novice grower. On the other hand, no other genus profits as dramatically as vandas from a more rigorous culture. Poorly grown plants produce flowers not recognizably the same as the identical plant grown well. The success of certain growers in obtaining large numbers of awards and trophies is largely a reflection of their sophisticated skills in growing vandas. Attention to detail is the key to growing vandas that fulfill their potential.

In terms of their culture, vandas share numerous similarities with genera such as *Cattleya*, *Phalaenopsis*, and *Dendrobium*. They also have numerous significant differences. Like *Phalaenopsis*, vandas have no bulbs for long-term water storage, and grow more or less continuously from a single growth point. Unlike *Phalaenopsis*, *Vanda* roots must have periods of drying. This latter trait, shared with cattleyas and dendrobiums (albeit to a lesser extent), reflects an adaptation to bright, airy natural environments. Understanding the special requirements of vandas is not difficult for experienced orchid growers, once the unique character of these plants is grasped. Vandas will tolerate, and perhaps even seem to thrive upon, a slightly improper regimen (one, for example, that might best suit a *Phalaenopsis*). But once a grower has seen them reach the summit of their potential, he or she will never be satisfied with less. Luckily, vandas are by nature cooperative, vigorous plants.

The goal of good *Vanda* culture, in both tropical gardens and temperate greenhouses, is simply to reproduce the conditions that naturally create this robust growth (and, if possible, to exceed nature). Vandas that are kept stress-free and uninterrupted in their growth produce flowers of such superlative quality that those who have seen them are no longer satisfied with the productivity of other orchid genera.

Culture Basics

Warmth

Warmth, more than any other factor, is the *sine qua non* of vigorous growth for vandas, which thrive best in temperatures between 60°F (15°C) and 90°F (32°C), but will tolerate both slightly higher and slightly lower temperatures. Both root and flower growth are most vigorous when night temperatures of 60–75°F (15–24°C) are combined with day temperatures in the range of 80–90°F (30–32°C). Such temperature swings are most easily obtained in temperate greenhouses. Here vandas can be grown to perfection if placed high and close to the glass, where the external temperatures are low but sunlight is abundant.

In North America, vandas are grown successfully as far north as Saskatchewan, Canada.

Widely thought of as strictly warm-growing, vandas are in fact best grown at the warm end of the intermediate range, preferring night temperatures in the upper 60s (about 20°C) and day temperatures in the mid-80s (about 28°C). In Florida, the cooler inland areas produce the best plants and flowers. In Thailand, the higher, cooler elevations upcountry, such as Nakon Sawon and Chiengmai, are more favorable than Bangkok and its environs. The effect of cooler temperatures is seen most strikingly in the warmer, more intense blues and reds—the result of an increased production of anthocyanins.

In adverse environmental conditions, vandas become semi-dormant, ceasing both root and leaf growth. No factor will produce this dormant state faster than chilling. Vandas should never be below 50°F (10°C) for more than a few hours. If *Vanda* leaves and root tissue are chilled below 50°F (10°C), dormancy will result. This condition is quickly apparent in the cessation of leaf and root growth. Leaves no longer unfold from the crown, and the green root tips withdraw until only a pinpoint of green appears at their ends. Once dormant, chilled plants require a fairly prolonged period of warmth before they resume growth. At the start of winter, such a setback could, at best, delay growth by a few weeks. But if warmth is not provided on a permanent basis, the plants may not resume normal vigorous growth until spring, thus losing up to ¼ of their annual growth. Vandas are opportunistic plants; they grow abundantly in favorable conditions, but react to adversity by cutting their losses with a retreat into dormancy.

In greenhouses, care should be taken to place vandas in the warmer sections and avoid drafts. In subtropical gardens, vandas can often be even more at risk than in temperate greenhouses, because they are unprotected from changes in the weather. Plants in exposed locations can be chilled rapidly by winds blowing over them at only marginally cold temperatures of around 50°F (10°C). In many areas where vandas are grown outside, cold fronts produce dormancy-inducing chills that are often enough to produce an effective cessation of growth for several months. Windbreaks of trees, hedges, plastic film, or wood greatly reduce chilling and permit vandas to maintain growth during the cooler months. Covering the plants or moving them to warmer locations, inside or out, will allow vandas to grow without interruption. Plants protected in this way will, in warm weather, start into rapid growth sooner and produce many more and finer flowers.

Although 50°F (10°C) is the threshold at which vandas are thrown into some degree of dormancy, the ideal minimum temperature is higher—60°F (15°C). As temperatures fall into this range, plants deficient in nutrients can show some stress. In particular, magnesium deficiency becomes apparent as a reddish pigmentation of the leaves (Plate 9-1). In subtropical settings, one should apply magnesium sulfate if temperatures are expected to fall below 70°F (20°C). This helps maintain plants at peak performance, and should of course be complemented by regular trace element fertilization. When proper nutrition is maintained, night temperatures in the range of 60–70°F (15–20°C) are actually beneficial, leading to increased production of roots and flowers.

High temperatures, above 92°F (34°C), are particularly damaging on a prolonged basis for *Vanda coerulea* and its hybrids (and, to a lesser degree, are bad for all vandas). Under such extremes, vandas have difficulty accumulating sufficient water and nutrients. In many tropical and subtropical areas, extreme daytime temperatures are abated by clouds or showers. Heavy misting or syringing in garden or greenhouse can mimic these conditions, providing extra water and, most importantly, lowering leaf temperature when temperatures are peaking in late morning or early afternoon. When leaves are cooled, vandas can subsequently withstand several hours of high air temperature.

Watering

Vandas require large quantities of water. A substantial portion of the total weight of a healthy *Vanda* is its root system. These highly absorbent, spongelike roots are the principal water-storage organs. They are capable of gathering and retaining water, but also require periods of dryness in order to maintain their health. When sufficient drying does not take place, vandas are prone to root rots caused by the ubiquitous water molds *Pythium* and *Phytophthora*. In addition to destroying roots, these fungi can enter the stem and progress upward until the entire plant is destroyed (Plate 9-2). Even if fungus is avoided, roots kept constantly wet are reluctant to throw new root tips. They are thus unable to supply enough new vegetative growth, and the result can be the eventual decline of the entire plant. Excessive or improper watering is the chief cause of poor results in the culture of vandas.

Vandas should be very heavily watered, to the point of saturation. Although light mists are sometimes beneficial to cool plants in exceptionally hot weather, excessive misting can wet roots without saturating them, leading to weakness and disease. Judging the best time to water vandas depends on several factors: light, temperature, air movement, and growing media are all critical. Close physical observation of the plants on a daily basis remains the best method to ascertain the plant's needs in its particular circumstances and environmental conditions (Plate 9-3).

The media and containers in which the plants are grown affects the watering schedule. Vandas grown in bark in plastic pots require less-frequent watering than plants in the same media in clay pots. Similarly, plants in slatted baskets filled with bark or lumps of charcoal require less-frequent watering than plants grown in bare wooden baskets. The age and quality of the media can also be a factor; although careful growers choose only the best and most lasting media, all eventually break down. Deteriorating media require a reduced water supply.

Exposure to light is also a critical factor in determining the watering regimen. Plants grown in bright light (above 4500 fc) need more water than those grown in dense shade, where metabolism is slower. In bright light, vandas show drought stress by becoming pale green or even yellow. In conditions of exceptionally bright light, intense heat, and clear skies, vandas may need to be watered as often as twice a day. Another effective strategy for vandas under heat stress is to water the plants in the afternoon when temperatures peak, but also early enough so that the plants are dry before evening.

Air movement also has a dramatic effect on the water requirement of vandas. When exposed to strong wind or other air movement, vandas are particularly vulnerable to drying. Often a large portion of their root mass is directly exposed on open baskets or clinging to the outside of pots. In such circumstances, vandas require frequent and heavy watering.

Other atmospheric conditions also affect watering patterns. When relative humidity is low, drying occurs more rapidly. As temperatures rise and air movement increases, the drying effect of low humidity is increased dramatically.

Root Color

Experienced growers come to know how their plants respond in their gardens and greenhouses, and the effects of their particular local climate. Nonetheless, one physiological observation is crucial to the correct watering of vandas, regardless of humidity, light, temperature, or air movement: the color of the roots. When dry, *Vanda* roots are white or pale gray; when saturated with water, they are overall dark green; when not completely wet, they are mottled white/green.

The first rule in watering vandas is to saturate the roots until they are overall dark green. This is best accomplished with two, three, or even four applications of water, spaced a minute or two apart. This interval allows the water applied to the surface of the root to be absorbed before more water is given. One way to tell whether a root or pot is ready for another application is to listen for the dripping of the water from them to stop. As the root absorbs a first dose of water, more water molecules are present to cohere to the water in the second and third application. When water begins to run off a root, no more water can be applied effectively to its surface. Under no circumstances should *Vanda* roots be left mottled green/white after watering. Always water until they are overall dark green.

If the root shows signs of severe dehydration, it may have difficulty absorbing water, because so few water molecules exist in the root to cohere to other molecules. In this case, the root acts like a cork in a wine bottle, initially repelling water. Soaking the plant or spacing the repeat watering slightly further apart can cure this problem.

Gradually, as they dry, *Vanda* roots return to a silvery white. When they are completely white, they should be watered again. The length of time required for a complete transformation will vary, but root color is the best indication of the need to water under all circumstances. Using this guideline, vandas can be watered daily in hot, dry weather and can go without water for several days in cooler, more humid conditions. One can apply no hard and fast rule in this respect, but vandas themselves will betray their needs in their root color.

The best watering device breaks the water into large droplets or numerous streams, so that coverage is rapid and thorough. A heavy-droplet misting head or a soft-watering rose is most effective. When watering a mixed collection of orchid genera in which vandas are hanging, it is desirable to water the vandas first, and then, when all the other types have been watered, return to the vandas and water them again. In this way, the *Vanda* roots will be able to absorb the first application, and the second will usually saturate them without causing any additional wetting of the foliage of the other orchids. If only the vandas require water, a heavy-mist head allows the wetting of the *Vanda* roots just to the point of run-off, thus maximizing the water on the roots' surface. In this way, plants beneath receive only minimal moisture to the upper surfaces of their leaves. If done in the morning, this will add humidity without creating fungus problems.

Feeding

Vandas are among the heavier-feeding orchids. They require much more fertilizer than paphiopedilums, and somewhat more fertilizer and more consistent feeding than dendrobiums and cattleyas. Like *Phalaenopsis*, vandas should be maintained in constant growth; hence, they require frequent and regular feeding. The best indicator of plant growth in vandas is the unfolding of leaves at the crown of the plant. This unfolding process should, ideally, continue unabated. Since vandas flower from the axils of their leaves, the higher the production of leaves, the greater the potential for flowers. An examination of the bases of the new leaves, just where they are emerging, should reveal a pale band of light green. This is newly produced leaf tissue that has not been exposed to light long enough to acquire chlorophyll. In rapidly growing vandas, such tissue is constantly produced and pushed from the apical meristem by the same process of intercalary growth that makes grass leaves grow.

A good fertilizer program will maintain plants with this pale band approximately 0.3 in (1 cm) broad. If the band is not visible or is less than 0.3 in (1 cm), insufficient fertilizer is being applied. In such cases, the rate or frequency of fertilization should be increased. Often, only an addition of ammonium nitrate or urea to increase nitrogen is all that is necessary. If vandas are being overfertilized, this will also be evident from observation of the unfolding leaves of the crown. The pale band at the apex will elongate to 0.75 in (2 cm) or more, and the entire top of the plant will start to bend under its own weight. If prolonged, this can lead to an unsightly bend in the plant. More importantly, such overfertilized plants are much more susceptible to disease. If plants show symptoms of overfertilization, they should be moved to brighter light to harden them, or fertilizer should be temporarily withdrawn and then resumed at a lower dosage.

Overall plant color also indicates the level of fertilizer. Ideally, mature plants should be a bright apple-green, a shade or so darker than a Granny Smith apple. Plants colored thus are growing well and are likely to flower. Seedlings can be maintained at a slightly darker shade by supplying higher levels of fertilizer or by growing them in lower light intensity, but mature plants cultivated in this way will produce lush growth and few flowers. Plants that are a lighter, yellow color are usually receiving too little fertilizer or water, or both. This usually occurs in bright situations. Such plants may produce numerous flower spikes, but with fewer, smaller flowers. Vandas under environmental distress often produce flowers that are so poor as to preclude the judging of their inherent quality. Well-fertilized and well-watered vandas are hard, turgid plants that produce their longest spikes and largest flowers.

Although vandas can be fed various dry fertilizers, both organic and inorganic, most growers use soluble fertilizers applied through hoses or irrigation systems. In practice, this is worked into the watering schedule of the plants. The best rule of thumb is to substitute fertilizer for water at about every fifth watering. The fertilizer schedule thus varies with the same environmental factors (heat, light, humidity, air movement) that influence watering. Liquid fertilizer, like water, should also be applied to dry roots in two or more sequential applications until roots are saturated and achieve a dark green color. Under bright, warm conditions when the plants are in full growth, a balanced fertilizer, usually 20-20-20, is applied at a rate of 2–3 lb per 100 gal of water (1 kg per 450 l) or 1.5–2 Tbs per gal (1 gm per 2 l). In cooler, darker conditions, this strength should be reduced. Under exceptionally bright conditions and very high temperatures, this rate of application may need to be increased.

HIGH PHOSPHORUS "BLOOM BOOSTERS"

Many growers alternate applications of balanced fertilizer with solutions high in phosphorus, such as 12-48-8 or 9-45-15. This is done on the assumption that higher levels of phosphorus encourage both roots and flowers. There is some truth in that assumption, and some benefit in this practice, but greater care needs to be taken to insure that the plants receive sufficient trace elements. This is particularly true when the water supply has a high pH, as this will cause the phosphorus to interfere more strongly with trace-element absorption.

An alternate approach is to supply additional phosphorus (through the use of these same formulas) at the times which are most critical; i.e., in spring, when the plants are rooting most vigorously, and in late summer and early fall, when blooms are anticipated and to be encouraged. Indeed, if initiation of bloom spikes is the goal, nothing is more effective than two or three successive applications of high-phosphorus fertilizer, applied when the first significant drop in temperature occurs. The combination of the environmental stress and the shock of the high-phosphorus fertilizer almost invariably induces bloom in mature hybrid vandas.

Dividing and Potting

One of the joys of *Vanda* culture is that these plants do not like to be disturbed—a characteristic that provides the perfect excuse for letting them grow in the same container for long periods. The same slatted wooden basket or clay pot can sustain a *Vanda* plant for many years, with the height of the plant adding to the grandeur of the floral display. Eventually, however, the plants become too tall to be managed easily or staked upright in the manner now conventionally used at exhibitions. When the plants do become too tall, cuttings must be taken from the top. The general rule is that top cuttings thrive best when they have three or more roots, but cuttings with only two well-developed roots may also be successful. Roots must be large enough to sustain the plant. In general, the less root that a cutting possesses, the more care in watering the newly establishing plant requires. Cuttings made in warm, humid weather are more easily induced to grow unimpeded. In cooler or dryer conditions, growth is slower, and cuttings may require misting several times a day to prevent dehydration and loss of the lower leaves.

Whenever possible, one should make top cuttings that allow one or more leaves to remain on the base of the plant. In making a cut into the leafy sections of a *Vanda* stem, one should remember that *Vanda* leaves sheathe both the stem and the bases of the leaves above them. *Vanda* stems are cut with a minimum of leaf loss and damage by passing the shears or knife down between the leaves along the stem and making a right-angle cut perpendicularly across the stem (Plate 9-4)—just as gladiolus flowers are cut to preserve the greatest stem length. Old stems left with at least one leaf will frequently produce two or more side shoots that often quickly develop into new flowering tops. When these in turn develop roots, they too can be removed.

Often, older plants that are in need of topping already have offshoots or *kiekis* ("babies," as the Hawaiians have dubbed them). These, like top cuttings, can be removed when they possess three or more roots. Many growers prefer to allow *kiekis* to flower at least once on the mother plant before removing them. The assumption is that such plants will flower sooner than unflowered offshoots.

Both top cuttings and *kiekis* must be fixed firmly into their new containers so that they root firmly to their pot or basket. Loose plants will not thrive, because their new roots are continually chafed away before they can make contact and adhere to the container. This is a problem with all orchids, but it is particularly acute with vandas because their stem length adds leverage to any disruptive movement, such as wind.

Normally, the bottom of a *Vanda* cutting is tied securely to the base of a slatted basket, and the stem is then tied to the top of the basket (Plates 9-5 to 9-7). On large cuttings, additional stakes and ties are sometimes necessary to ensure that the plant is immobilized until it has established itself. Once properly secured to a sufficiently large container, a *Vanda* cutting should quickly re-root and need no further potting for many years.

Appendix A

Troubleshooting Guide for *Vanda* Culture

Problem
    Possible Cause   Solution

Root growth stops

Possible Cause	Solution
Too cold	Avoid chilling below 50°F (10°C) or placing plants in cold drafts
Too dry	Thoroughly saturate roots with water until they turn dark green. Water again when white
Thrips or mites	Look for signs of infestation. Thrips damage occurs as a ring at the point that the new root matures (Plate 9-8). Mites can be seen with a hand lens. Most prevalent during periods of dry weather. Spray with soap to control both, or spray recommended pesticides

Problem
    Possible Cause   Solution

Root growth stops, then restarts
    Excessive fertilizer   Fertilizer burn starts as browning at the new
                                      root tips. Lower the dosage of fertilizer
                                      and the frequency of application
    Excessive salts in water   Water supplies containing high levels of
                                      dissolved salts are undesirable. If none
                                      other is available, always water heavily
                                      and avoid misting, or salts will
                                      accumulate on root tips
    Thrips   Look for signs of damage (see above), spray
                                      recommended pesticides

Leaves do not unfold from crown
    Too little water   First, ensure root saturation on each
                                      watering, then increase frequency of
                                      applications
    Too little fertilizer   Increase frequency, then dosage, of fertilizer
    Too cold   Maintain above 50°F (10°C)
    Disease prevalent in   Crown rot is caused by pathogens, *Pythium*
        crown   or *Phytophthora*, usually referred to as
                                      water molds. Dose with 3% hydrogen
                                      peroxide. Spray with Metalaxyl, Alumin
                                      tris(-O-ethy phosphorate), or 5-Ethoxyl-
                                      3-trichloromethy-1,2,4-thiadiazole

Leaves turn pale yellow
    Too little water   Increase frequency of watering
    Too little fertilizer   Increase concentration of nitrogen level of
                                      fertilizer, or increase frequency
    Trace element deficiency   Supply micronutrients
    Too much light   Increase shade
    Too hot   Increase air circulation

| Problem | |
| Possible Cause | Solution |

Leaves turn dark green

Too little light	Increase light
Too much nitrogen	Decrease level or frequency of fertilization
Too much phosphorus	Lower phosphorus level in fertilizer

Irregularly shaped spots appear suddenly on leaves

| Sunburn | Move plant to more shaded location |

Rounded, sunken spots appear on leaves

| *Cercaspora* fungus (Plate 9-9) | Increase light and air movement; spray with copper hydroxide or Mancozeb |

Raised streaks or diamond-shaped lesions appear on lower leaves

| *Phyllosticata capitalensis* Henn. fungus (Plate 9-10) | Remove infected leaves, spray with triflorine |

Leaves and roots become covered with white cobweb-like growth, roots with ginger-colored beads

| Southern blight (*Sclerotium*) (Plate 9-11) | Spray with Terraclor |

Plant does not flower

Too little light	Move to brighter location
Too much nitrogen	Decrease nitrogen, increase phosphorus and potassium in fertilizer solution
Temperature too constant	Vandas bloom best when there is a change, not too extreme, in day to night temperature

Problem
    Possible Cause   Solution

Immature flower spikes fail
    Thrips or mite damage in   Spray recommended pesticides
        leaf axil
    Drought stress   Increase watering

Flowers drop
    Thrips or mite damage   Spray recommended pesticides
    Drought stress   Increase water

Flowers turn brown at edges
    Thrips damage   Spray recommended pesticides

Appendix B

Species in
Vanda

Prepared by Eric A. Christenson, Ph.D.
Amended by Martin R. Motes, Ph.D.

Species in *Vanda* (some provisionally)

V. alpina (Lindl.) Lindl.

V. arcuata J. J. Sm.

V. bensonii Batem.

V. brunnea Reichb.f.

V. chlorosantha (Garay) E. A. Christ.

V. coerulea Griff. ex Lindl.

V. coerulescens Griff.

V. concolor Bl.

V. crassiloba Teijsm. & Binn.

V. cristata Lindl.

V. dearei Reichb.f.

V. denisoniana Benson & Reichb.f.

V. devoogtii J. J. Sm.

V. drakei Reichb.f.

V. flabellata (Rolfe ex Downie) E. A. Christ.

V. foetida J. J. Sm.

V. fuscoviridis Lindl.

V. griffithii Lindl.

V. hastifera Reichb.f.

V. helvola Bl.

V. hindsii Lindl.

V. insignis Bl.

V. javieriae Tiu

V. kwantungensis Cheng & Tang

V. lamellata Lindl.

V. leucostele Schltr.

V. lilacina Teijsm. & Binn.

V. *limbata* Bl.

V. *lindenii* Reichb.f.

V. *liouvillei* Finet

V. *lombokensis* J. J. Sm.

V. *luzonica* Loher ex Rolfe

V. *merrillii* Ames & Quisumb.

V. *pumila* J. D. Hook.

V. *punctata* Ridl.

V. *roeblingiana* Rolfe

V. *sanderiana* Reichb.f.

V. *saxatilis* J. J. Sm.

V. *scandens* Holtt.

V. *stangeana* Reichb.f.

V. *subconcolor* Tang & Wang

V. *sumatrana* Schltr.

V. *tessellata* (Roxb.) W. J. Hook. ex G. Don

V. *testacea* (Lindl.) Reichb.f.

V. *thwaitesii* J. D. Hook.

V. *tricolor* Lindl.

Species synonymized in or transferred from *Vanda*

V. *amesiana* Reichb.f. = *Holcoglossum amesiana* (Reichb.f.) E. A. Christ.

V. *amiensis* Masamune & Segawa = sphalm. for V. *yamiensis* Ma. & Seg. = V. *lamellata* Lindl.

V. *batemanni* Lindl. = *Vandopsis lissochiloides* (Gaud.) Pfitz.

V. *bicaudata* Thw. = *Diploprora championii* J. D. Hook.

V. *boxallii* (Reichb.f.) Reichb.f. = V. *lamellata* Lindl.

V. *cathcartii* Lindl. = *Esmeralda cathcartii* (Lindl.) Reichb.f.

V. *clarkei* (J. D. Hook.) N. E. Br. = *Esmeralda clarkei* (J. D. Hook.) Reichb.f.

V. *clitellaria* Reichb.f. = V. *lamellata* Lindl.

V. *congesta* Lindl. = *Acampe congesta* (Lindl.) Lindl.

V. *cumingii* Lodd. = V. *lamellata* Lindl.

V. *denevei* Zurowetz = *Paraphal. denevei* (J. J. Sm.) A. D. Hawkes

V. *densiflora* Lindl. = *Rhynchostylis gigantea* (Lindl.) Ridl.

V. *doritoides* Guill. = *Ornithochilus deavayi* Finet

V. *esquirolei* Schltr. = V. *concolor* Bl.

V. *falcata* Beer = *Neofinetia falcata* (Thunb.) Hu

V. *fasciata* Gardn. ex Lindl. = *Acampe praemorsa* (Roxb.) Blatter & McCann

V. *fimbriata* Gardn. ex Thw. = *Gastrochilus acaulis* (Lindl.) Ktze.

V. furva Lindl. = *V. concolor* Bl.

V. gibbsiae Rolfe = *V. hastifera* Reichb.f.

V. gigantea Lindl. = *Vandopsis gigantea* (Lindl.) Pfitz.

V. guibertii Lindl. = *Trichoglottis guibertii* (Lindl.) J. J. Sm.

V. hainanensis Rolfe = *Rhynchostylis gigantea* (Lindl.) Ridl.

V. henryi Schltr. = *V. denisoniana* Bens. & Reichb.f.

V. hookeri hort. = *Papilionanthe hookeriana* (Reichb.f.) Garay

V. hookeriana Reichb.f. = *Papilionanthe hookeriana* (Reichb.f.) Garay

V. kimballiana Reichb.f. = *Holcoglossum kimballianum* (Reichb.f.)
    Garay

V. laotica Guill. = *V. lilacina* Teijsm. & Binn.

V. lindleyana Griff. ex Lindl. & Paxt. = *Vandopsis gigantea* (Lindl.)
    Pfitz.

V. lissochiloides Lindl. = *Vandopsis lissochiloides* (Gaud.) Pfitz.

V. longifolia Lindl. = *Acampe rigida* (Buch.-Ham. ex J. J. Sm.) Hunt

V. lowii Lindl. = *Dimorphorchis lowii* (Lindl.) Rolfe

V. masperoae Guill. Apud Gagnep. = *Papilionanthe pedunculata*
    (Kerr) Garay

V. michoholtlitzii Rolfe = *V. denisoniana* Benson & Reichb.f.

V. multiflora Lindl. = *Acampe rigida* (Buch.-Ham. ex J. E. Sm.) Hunt

V. nasugbuana Parsons = *V. lamellata* Lindl.

V. obliqua Wall. ex J. D. Hook. = *Gastrochilus obliquum* Lindl.

V. paniculata (Ker.-Gawl.) R. Br. = *Cleisostoma paniculatum*
    (Ker.-Gawl.) Garay

V. parishii Veitch & Reichb.f. = *Hygrochilus parishii*
    (Veitch & Reichb.f.) Engl. & Prantl.

V. parviflora Lindl. = *V. testacea* (Lindl.) Reichb.f.

V. pauciflora Breda = *Thrixspermum* sp.

V. peduncularis Lindl. = *Cottonia peduncularis* (Lindl.) Reichb.f.

V. petersiana Schltr. = *V. stangeana* Reichb.f.

V. pseudo-coerulescens Guill. = *Rhynchostylis coelestis* Reichb.f.

V. pulchella Wight = *Gastrochilus acaulis* (Lindl.) Ktze.

V. pusilla Teijsm. & Binn. = *Trichoglottis pusilla* Reichb.f.

V. recurva W. J. Hook. = *Cleisostoma rostratum* (Lindl.) Garay

V. rostrata Lodd. = *Cleisostoma rostratum* (Lindl.) Garay

V. roxburghii R. Br. = *V. tessellata* (Roxb.) W. J. Hook. ex G. Don

V. rupestris Hand.-Mazz. = *Holcoglossum rupestre* (Hand.-Mazz.) Garay

V. saprophytica Gagnep. = *Holcoglossum saprophyticum* (Gagnep.) E. A. Christ.

V. scripta Sprenga. = *Grammatophyllum speciosum* B.

V. simondii Gagnep. = *Cleisostoma simondii* (Gagnep.) Seid.

V. spathulata (L.) Spreng. = *Taprobanea spathulata* E. A. Christ.

V. storiei Storie ex Reichb.f. = *Renanthera storiei* Reichb.f.

V. striata Reichb.f. = *V. cristata* Lindl.

V. suaveolens Bl. = *V. tricolor* Lindl.

V. suavis Lindl. = *V. tricolor* Lindl.

V. suavis F. V. Muell. = *V. hindsii* Lindl.

V. subulifolia Reichb.f. = *Holcoglossum subulifolium* (Reichb.f.) E. A. Christ.

V. sulingii Bl. = *Armodorum sulingii* (Bl.) Reichb.f.

V. superba Lindl. = *V. lamellata* Lindl.

V. tawaniana S. S. Ting = (*Luisia* cf. *egasepala* × *Papilionanthe*)

V. teres Lindl. = *Papilionanthe teres* (Roxb.) W. J. Hook. ex G. Don

V. trichorhiza W. J. Hook. = *Luisia trichorhiza* (W. J. Hook.) Bl.

V. tricuspidata J. J. Sm. = *Papilionanthe tricuspidata* (J. J. Sm.) Garay

V. truncata J. J. Sm. = *V. hindsii* Lindl.

V. undulata Lindl. = *Vandopsis undulata* (Lindl.) J. J. Sm.

V. unicolor Steud. = *V. lamellata* Lindl. and *V. tessellata* (Roxb.) W. J. Hook. ex G. Don

V. vidalii Boxall ex Naves = *V. lamellata* Lindl.

V. viminea Guill. = *Acampe rigida* (Buch.-Ham. ex J. E. Sm.) Hunt

V. violacea Lindl. = *Rhynchostylis gigantea* ssp. *violacea* (Lindl.) E. A. Christ.

V. vipanii Reichb.f. = *V. liouvillei* Finet

V. vitellina Kraenzl. = *V. parviflora* Lindl.

V. watsoni Rolfe = *Holcoglossum subulifolium* (Reichb.f.) E. A. Christ.

V. whiteana Herbert & Blake = *V. hindsii* Lindl.

V. wightiana Lindl. ex Wight = *Acampe praemorsa* (Roxb.) Blatter & McCann

V. yamiensis Mas. & Seg. = sphalm. for *V. amiensis* Mas. & Seg. = *V. lamellata* Lindl.

Dubious species

V. *arbuthnotianum* Kraenzl.
V. *cruenta* Lindl.
V. *bicolor* Griff.
V. *jainii* Chauhan

Natural hybrids

V. ×*amoena* = V. *coerulea* × V. *tessellata*
V. ×*boumaniae* J. J. Sm.
V. ×*charlesworthii* = V. *coerulea* × V. *bensonii*
V. ×*confusa* Rolfe = V. *coerulescens* × V. *lilacina*
V. ×*moorei* Rolfe = V. *coerulea* × V. *kimballiana*

Glossary

anthocyanins—pigments in flowers that produce blue and red colors.

caudicle—the stalklike structure that attaches the pollen masses to the viscidium.

concolor—of one, more or less uniform, color over the entire flower.

cultivar—literally, a cultivated variety of plant.

grex—literally, a flock; hence, all of the plants produced from one particular crossing of two parents. Subsequent crosses of the same parents are also considered to be the same grex.

intergeneric—a hybrid between two plants belonging to separate natural or artificial genera.

introgression—the passage of genes from one species into another as natural hybrids breed back to one of the parent species through several generations.

mericlone—a plant reproduced asexually from undifferentiated tissue.

mericloning—the process by which plants are reproduced asexually from meristematic tissue.

midlobes—parts of the lip, usually partly or entirely surrounding the column, and hence important in pollination mechanics and species differentiation.

picotte—a line or fringe of bordering color distinct from the overall flower color.

praemorse—giving the appearance of having been bitten off, as the ragged edged ends of *Vanda* leaves.

semiterete—the deeply V-ed leaf shape that results from crossing terete-leaved species to broader leaved species or hybrids. Formerly incorrectly applied to species in the genus *Holcoglossum*.

terete—rounded or pencil-shaped, as the leaves of certain species of several genera. Those in the genus *Papilionanthe* were long considered vandas.

vandaceous—a horticultural term used to describe the large group of plants related to vandas that is more properly referred to as Aeridinae or Sarcanthinae.

Vandanthe—the proper epithet for hybrids between *Vanda* and *Euanthe*.

viscidium—the sticky disk to which pollen is connected as a means to attach it to potential pollinators.

Bibliography

Arditti, J. 1977. *Orchid Biology: Reviews and Perspectives*. Ithaca, N.Y.: Cornell University Press.

Backer, C. A., and R. C. Bakhuizen. 1968. *The Flora of Java*. Groningen.

Banerji, M. L. 1982. *Orchids of Nepal*. Dehra Dun, India: Jayyed Press.

Barnes, Carson. 1990. Mad Dogs, Englishmen, and Vandas. *American Orchid Society Bulletin* 59: 999.

Bateman, J. 1867. *Second Century of Orchidaceous Plants*. London: L. Reeve & Co.

Bentham, G., and J. D. Hooker. 1883. Orchideae. In *Genera Plantarum*, vol. 3. London: L. Reeve & Co.

Cheng S., and C. Z. Tang. 1986. The Study on Genus *Vanda* in *China* (Orchidaceae). *Acta Bot. Yunnan* 8 (2): 216–221. Rpt. & Trans. 1988. *The Orchid Digest* 52: 38–46.

Christenson, Eric A. 1994. Taxonomy of the Aeridinae with an Infrageneric Classification of *Vanda* Jones ex R. Br. *Proceedings of the 14th World Orchid Conference* (Glasgow) 206.

Comber, J. B. 1982. The Genus *Vanda* in Java. *The Orchid Digest* 46: 125–129.

Cribb, Phillip, H. P. Bechtel, and E. Launert. 1981. *The Manual of Cultivated Orchid Species.* Cambridge, Mass.: M.I.T. Press.

Darwin, Charles. 1862. *On the Various Contrivances by which British and Foreign Orchids are Fertilised by Insects.* London: J. Murray.

Davis, R., and M. Steiner. 1952. *Philippine Orchids.* New York: William-Frederick Press.

Dockrill, A. W. 1967. *Australian Sarcanthinae.* Sydney: The Australian Native Orchid Society.

Dodson, Calaway, and Robert Gillespie. 1967. *The Biology of the Orchids.* Nashville: Mid-America Orchid Congress Inc.

Dressler, Robert. 1974. Classification of the Orchid Family. *Proceedings of the 7th World Orchid Congress* (Medellin, Colombia) 259–278.

———. 1981. *The Orchids: Natural History and Classification.* Cambridge, Mass.: Harvard University Press.

———. 1993. *Phylogeny and Classification of the Orchid Family.* Portland, Or.: Dioscorides Press.

Freed, Hugo. 1979. *New Horizons in Orchid Breeding.* Pomona, Ca.: Day Printing Corporation.

Gagnepain, F., and A. Guillaumin. 1932. Orchidacées. In *Flore Générale de L'Indochine*, vol. 2. Paris: Masson.

Garay, L., and H. Sweet. 1974. *Orchids of the Southern Ryukyu Islands.* Cambridge, Mass.: Botanical Museum, Harvard University.

Grant, Bartle. 1895. *The Orchids of Burma.* Rangoon: Hanthawaddy Press.

Groeneveldt, H. 1952. Vandas: *Vanda suavis, Vanda sanderae,* and *Vanda tricolor. The Orchid Review* 43–44.

Grove, David L. 1983. Strap Leaf Vandas. AOS *Awards Quarterly* 14: 3.

———. 1984. *Vanda coerulea*—Queen of the Vandas. *American Orchid Society Bulletin* 53: 612–618.

———. 1995. *Vandas and Ascocendas.* Portland, Or.: Timber Press.

Hawkes, A. D. 1965. *Encyclopaedia of Cultivated Orchids.* London: Faber and Faber Ltd.

Hawkes, Alex. 1952. Some Beautiful *Vanda* Hybrids. *The Orchid Journal* 1: 72.

Holttum, R. E. 1964. Orchids of Malaya. *Flora of Malaya*, vol. 1. Singapore: Government Printing Offices.

Hooker, J. D. 1890. Orchideae. *Flora of British India*, vols. 5 and 6. Rpt. 1988. Dehra Dun, India: Shiva Offset Press.

Hu, Shiu-ying. 1977. *The Genera of Orchidaceae in Hong Kong*. Hong Kong: The Chinese University Press.

International Orchid Commission. 1976. *Handbook of Orchid Nomenclature*. 2nd ed. London: I.O.C.

Jayaweera, D. M. A. 1981. Orchidaceae. *Flora of Ceylon*, vol. 2. New Delhi: Oxford and IBH.

Kamemoto, H., and R. Sagarik. 1975. *Beautiful Thai Orchids*. Bangkok: The Orchid Society of Thailand.

Kennedy, George. 1979. Some Monopodial Orchids, Part 1: The Genus *Vanda*. *The Orchid Digest* 43: 45–50.

Lavarack, P. S., and B. Gray. 1985. *Tropical Orchids of Australia*. Melbourne: Thoman Nelson.

Lindley, J. 1852–59. *Folia Orchidacea*. London: J. Matthews.

Northern, Rebecca. 1970. *Home Orchid Growing*. New York: Reinhold.

Millar, Andree. 1978. *Orchids of Papua New Guinea*. Seattle: University of Washington Press.

Motes, Martin. 1988. Unraveling a Rainbow. *American Orchid Society Bulletin* 57: 709, 854, 949, 1107, 1224, 1341.

———. 1989. The New *Vanda* Scene in South Florida. *The Florida Orchidist* 32: 179–189.

———. 1990. The Influence of Species on Modern *Vanda* Hybridization. *Proceedings of the 13th World Orchid Conference* (Auckland) World Orchid Conference Trust.

———. 1992. New Directions in *Vanda* Breeding. *Proceedings of the 4th Asian Pacific Orchid Conference* (Chaingmai, Thailand).

———. 1994. *Vanda tricolor* var. *suavis*: The sweet smelling *Vanda*. *The Orchid Digest* 58.

O'Byrne, Peter. 1990. *Survey of Lowland Orchids of Papua New Guinea*. Melbourne: Australian Orchid Foundation.

Orchid Society of South East Asia. 1993. *Orchid Growing in the Tropics*. Singapore: Times Editions.

Pradhan, U. C. 1976–79. *Indian Orchids: Guide to Indentification and Culture*. 2 vols. Kalimpong: n.p.

Quisumbing, Eduardo A. 1981. *The Complete Writings on Philippine Orchids*. Ed. Helen L. Valmayor. Manila: Eugenio Lopez Foundation.

Raizada, M., H. Naithani, and H. Saxena. 1981. *Orchids of Mussoorie*. Dehra Dun, India: Shiva Printers.

Rakpaibulsombat, Somsak. 1992. *Thai Orchid Species*. Bangkok: Suriwong Book Centre.

Reinikka, M. 1995. *A History of the Orchid*. Portland, Or.: Timber Press.

Rentoul, J. N. 1991. *Growing Orchids: The Hybrid Story*. Portland, Or: Timber Press.

Sanders, F. 1927. *Sander's Orchid Guide*. St. Albans: Sanders.

Schlecter, R. 1982. *The Orchidaceae of German New Guinea*. Ed. D. F. Blaxell. Melbourne: Australian Orchid Foundation.

Seidenfaden, Gunnar. 1988. *Orchid Genera in Thailand XIV. Fifty-nine Vandoid Genera*. Opera Botanica 95. Copenhagen: Nordic Publications.

Seidenfaden, Gunnar, and T. Smitinand. 1959–64. *Orchids of Thailand*. Vols. 1–4. Bangkok: The Siam Society.

Seidenfaden, Gunnar, and J. Wood. 1992. *The Orchids of Peninsular Malaysia and Singapore*. Fredensborg, Denmark: Olsen and Olsen.

Smith, J. J. 1905. Die Orchideen von Java. *Flora von Buitenzorg*, vol. 6. Leiden: E. J. Brill.

Sophonsiri, Treekul. 1985. New Trends in *Vanda* Breeeding. *Proceedings of the World Orchid Conference* (Miami) World Orchid Conference Trust.

Sweet, Herman R. 1980. *The Genus Phalaenopsis*. Pomona, California: The Orchid Digest Inc.

Tan, K. W. 1975. Taxonomy of *Arachnis, Armordorum, Esmeralda*, and *Dimorphorchis. Selbyana* 1: 1–15.

Teo, K. H. Chris. 1985. *Native Orchids of Peninsular Malaysia.* Singapore: Times Books International.

Valmayor, Helen L. 1984. *Orchidiana Philippiniana.* Manila: Eugenio Lopez Foundation.

Veitch, J. 1887–94. *A Manual of Orchidaceous Plants.* Chelsea: J. Veitch and Sons.

Williams, Benjamin. 1894. *The Orchid Growers' Manual.* London: Victoria and Paradise.

Withner, C. 1959. *The Orchids—A Scientific Survey.* New York: Ronald.

Index of
Botanical Names

The abbreviations Pl., Pls. refer to color plates.